THE *Greatest* **TRIVIA** **QUIZ** BOOK

First published in Great Britain in 1996 by
Parragon Book Service Ltd.
Unit 13–17
Avonbridge Trading Estate
Atlantic Road
Avonmouth
Bristol BS11 9QD

ISBN 0-7525-1088-6

Edited, designed & produced by Haldane Mason, London
Printed in India

Acknowledgements:
Art Direction: Ron Samuels
Editors: Alexa Stace, Diana Vowles
Design: Anthony Limerick, Somewhere Creative
Picture Research: Jackum Brown & Vicky Walters

CONTENTS

INTROD

UCTION

The appetite for trivia, once acquired, can be insatiable, so here is a new bumper collection of nearly 3,000 questions to tease, torment and entertain. You can use them to test yourself, put your friends on the spot or organize your own quiz night.

The book is divided into several subject categories, which cover every aspect of life, whether ancient or modern, human or animal, spiritual or environmental. You can roam the world with Geography and Travel, delve into history with Past and Present or relax and enjoy yourself with Popular Culture or Sport and Leisure. Meet or re-meet Famous Folk and get practical with Indoors and Out. Some quizzes in Youth World will start you reminiscing, others are set to appeal to the kid in all of us. Pot Luck

aims to take you by surprise, so 'anything goes' with the subjects.

Each quiz has an assortment of questions, in random order. Some are dead easy, some will have you delving deep into your memory banks and others could stump you unless you have a working knowledge of the subject. Some will suit the older members of the family, while for others you may need help from the younger generation.

To meet the Greatest Trivia challenge you need quick reactions, a good store of general knowledge – and luck! Every trivia addict knows how maddening it is when they can answer their opponent's question but not their own. It's all in the game and who cares who wins, so long as everyone has fun!

How To

ULTIMATE TRIVIA GAMES

You can use the Greatest Trivia Quizzes just as you like, sitting alone, or with competitive teams. Here are three suggestions for games you might like to play, but try ringing the changes by making up your own rules.

Game 1

Single player

Pick your favourite from the seven subject categories (*not* including Pot Luck) and try to answer each question in order, scoring 1 point for each correct answer. Every time you fail to answer, take a question from Pot Luck 1. If you answer correctly, score 2 points, if not, deduct 1 point from your current score. When you have exhausted the questions in Pot Luck 1, the game is over. Next time you can begin again from where you left off, using Pot Luck 2, and competing against your last score.

Play

Game 2

2 or more players or teams

Each player or team picks a subject, which can include Pot Luck. You can cut cards or throw dice to decide who chooses first – or you can make the game more difficult by putting all the categories in a hat and making a random choice. Decide in advance how long you want the game to last, then go through the book with each player or team taking turns to answer question 1 in their chosen category, then question 2. Score 2 points for each correct answer. The winner is the person or team with most points when time is up. For the next round, start again where you left off.

Game 3

Several teams with 3 or more members, and a quiz master

Put numbers from 1 to 25 in a hat. Each team draws a number and tries to answer that number in one quiz after another each time their turn comes round. The questions are not graded for difficulty, so no team is at a disadvantage and team members can confer over their answers. Each correct answer in the subject categories earns 1 point, but each time a Pot Luck question is answered correctly, the team score is doubled. The game can be played over again with each team drawing a second number and proceeding through the book in the same way.

Q 9

3. Geneva stands at the tip of Lake Geneva. What do the Swiss call the lake?

4. In which city would you find elegant shopping streets called Via Morte, Via Napoleone, Via Manzoni and Via Spiga?

5. What do Les Halles in Paris and Covent Garden in London have in common?

6. Which city is known as the 'Venice of the North'?

7. From San Francisco, which prison, now closed, can be visited across the bay?

8. In which city is the house in which Anne Frank and her family hid from the Nazis?

9. In which part of Bangkok would you find the Temple of the Emerald Buddha?

10. Which German city has a chiming clock on its medieval town hall, with two tiers of dancing and jousting figures which emerge twice daily?

11. Name the square, called 'Heavenly Peace' in English, which lies at the heart of Beijing.

12. Which street is Dublin's main shopping centre?

1. The Gran Teatre del Liceu is one of the world's finest opera houses. In which city is it located?

13. What style of architecture is the Parthenon in Athens?

2. What was built in Berlin in 1788 as a victory arch for triumphant Prussian armies?

14. In which district in Paris would you find the Sacré-Coeur and the Place du Tertre, where painters gather?

15. Visitors who wish to return to Rome must throw a coin into which fountain?

16. The Taj Mahal can be visited in which Indian city?

17. Which city is sometimes called the 'Paris of the East' and sometimes 'the Whore of China'?

18. The Rockefeller Plaza in New York is used as an open-air cafe in summer. What is it in winter?

19. Where would you be if you could look out over the city from Victoria Peak?

20. In Brussels the small bronze statue of a boy urinating is called the 'Mannekin Pis'. What is the statue nicknamed?

21. In which city could you climb the Spanish Steps?

22. One of the great landmarks of Sydney was designed by Jorn Utzon and finished in 1973. What is it?

23. The Dome of the Rock was built in 691 by the caliph Abd-al-Malik. Where is it?

24. At the famous café in Venice's Piazza San Marco an orchestra plays to patrons. What is the name of the café?

25. Which is the only New York museum with architecture as famous as its collection?

1. Louis Armstrong's nickname was Satchmo. What does it stand for?

2. What was the name of King Oliver's famous jazz band?

3. What is Bix Beiderbecke's chief claim to fame?

4. What is the two-fisted style of piano playing built on ragtime emphasizing tenths in the bass called?

5. What is Jelly Roll Morton's real name?

6. Who was known as the 'King of Swing'?

7. What are the first names of the Marsalis brothers?

8. Who is famous for using the vibraphone in jazz?

9. With what style of jazz is US saxophonist Grover Washington associated?

10. Who was known as 'Lady Day'?

11. What was Glenn Miller's signature tune?

12. Gene Krupa is widely rated the greatest jazz musician on what instrument?

13. Which city is the home of jazz?

14. Who was the leader of the 'Hot Club of France'?

15. What instrument does Stephane Grappelli play?

16. What was the real name of Leadbelly, the great blues singer?

17. Dizzy Gillespie and Charlie Parker were the chief creators and exponents of what type of jazz?

18. Whose albums include *Birth of the Cool*, *Sketches of Spain* and *Bitches' Brew*?

19. The 1940s were the 'big band' era. How many players were needed for a 'big band'?

20. Which instrument did jazz musician John Coltrane play?

21. What name was given to the piano jazz that used a repeated motif for the left hand?

22. Whose numbers included 'Mood Indigo', 'Black and Tan Fantasy' and 'Sophisticated Lady'?

23. Which instruments were dominant in the Dixieland jazz style?

24. Who brought the tenor saxophone to prominence as a jazz instrument?

25. Which type of jazz did Lionel Hampton, Stan Getz and Miles Davis develop in reaction to hot bebop?

6. Japanese cedars have bright green leaves in summer. What colour are they in winter?

7. Are whitebeams and mountain ash deciduous or evergreen?

8. *Acer saccharum* produces large areas of bright colour in New England in the fall. What is its everyday name?

9. Arbutus is known as the 'strawberry tree'. Why?

10. To which family do gorse and broom belong?

11. For which flowering tree is Japan famous?

12. Why is it a poor idea to plant a rhus in a lawn?

13. The Judas tree, native to the Mediterranean region, has flowers which hang in clusters on twigs and branches. What colour are they?

14. Which trees have reached giant proportions in California and Oregon?

15. The leaves of the mulberry tree are the favourite food of which creature?

16. How do willow and poplar trees reproduce?

17. The kowhai has small yellow flowers grown in clusters. It is the national flower of which country?

18. Basswood is a lime tree with white flowers. What shape are the leaves?

1. What is the fruit of the hickory tree?

2. Who is supposed to have brought the sycamore tree to Britain?

3. How are maples and limes pollinated?

4. What type of flowers does the yucca have?

5. What is the wood at the centre of the tree stem called?

19. When growing fruit trees, cordons are one of the best types for a small garden. What shape is a cordon?

20. What is the popular name of the pyracantha?

21. Rhododendrons and azaleas belong to the same genus. Which of them is deciduous?

22. Gum-trees are mainly natives of Australia. What is their proper name?

23. Which family of trees do junipers belong to?

24. The flower of which tree is called May blossom?

25. What is the national tree of Lebanon?

1. How many bits make a byte?

2. What do the letters RAM stand for?

3. In which decade did pocket calculators first make their appearance?

4. In the computer world, what is nicknamed Big Blue?

5. What name is given to the type of printer which makes up each character from a pattern of dots?

6. Goods in shops are often marked with a pattern of black and white stripes. What is this called?

7. The earliest type of robot was a water-clock invented in 250BC. In which country?

8. Name the satellite launched into space in July 1962 and used to send live TV programmes across the Atlantic.

9. What are FORTRAN, PASCAL and COBOL?

10. In which decade was the compact disc developed?

11. At the moment, phone calls travel as electricity along copper cables but they can be sent as light along thin strands of glass. What are these called?

12. Modern computers operate at a speed of up to 400 megaflops. What is a megaflop?

13. The film Star Wars featured two lovable robots. What were their names?

14. When using a bank card in a cash dispenser, customers use a PIN. What do the initials stand for?

15. What is the usual term for an input device used to move an on-screen pointer or cursor to select commands?

16. Name the device that takes information from the computer and modifies it so that it can be transmitted along ordinary phone lines.

17. What do the initials ROM stand for?

18. In which decade did the first minature TV sets appear?

19. A fax machine is used to send or receive documents. What is fax short for?

20. Synthesizers are complex pieces of electronic equipment. What do they combine with a computer?

21. As part of a computer, what does a clock chip do?

22. Robot is a word coined by Czech playwright Karel Capek from the word 'robota'. What does it mean?

23. What does interactive cable TV enable viewers to do?

24. What is CAD?

25. A microwriter is an electronic word processor but it lacks one major feature of a standard word processor. What is it?

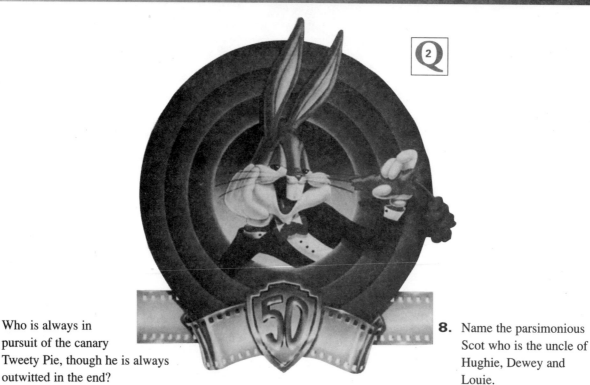

1. Who is always in pursuit of the canary Tweety Pie, though he is always outwitted in the end?

2. What is Bugs Bunny's catchphrase?

3. Why are the popular Tom and Jerry cartoons often criticized?

4. Name the cartoon cat who 'kept on walking'.

5. Where do the Flintstones live?

6. What breed of dog is Snoopy from the Peanuts cartoon?

7. Who has a girl-friend named Olive Oyl?

8. Name the parsimonious Scot who is the uncle of Hughie, Dewey and Louie.

9. Who created the girls of St Trinians?

10. In the TV series *Star Trek*, Mr Spock is played by Leonard Nimoy. Who is Spock's voice in the cartoon series?

11. Mickey Mouse first appeared in 1928, in a short silent film. What was it called?

12. What is Mr Magoo's handicap?

13. Name the sexy cartoon character with a squeaky voice and big eyes who appeared in short films like *Red Hot Mama* and *Zula Hula* in the 1930s.

14. Who created Scooby Doo?

15. Who has the reputation as the fastest mouse in Mexico?

16. Which ancient Gaul, originally featured in strip cartoons, became the star of several French animated films?

17. Which bird, found in the North American deserts, has become a cartoon character who zooms along like a car at full speed?

18. Chip 'n' Dale are two lively, clever chipmunks. What is the difference in appearance between them?

19. What breed of dog is Pluto?

20. Where is Popeye's home?

21. On whose adventures is the cartoon Willy Fog based?

22. How old was Donald Duck in 1994?

23. In *Who Framed Roger Rabbit?*, what is the name of Roger's curvaceous wife?

24. In which cartoon would you find Elmer Fudd?

25. Whose neighbours are Barney and Betty Rubble?

Q 12

4. Which Ugandan president deposed Milton Obote and expelled the Asian community?

5. Norman Manley was Prime Minister of Jamaica from 1959 to 1962. His son became Prime Minister in 1972. What was his name?

6. As dictator of Haiti he was known as 'Papa Doc'. What was his name?

7. Who was Secretary General of the United Nations from 1962 to 1971?

8. As leader of the Nationalist Congress Party of India, he was imprisoned by the British nine times. Name him.

9. How did Heinrich Himmler meet his death?

10. What was British Prime Minister Gladstone's middle name?

11. Ivan IV united Russia but in the later years of his reign his actions earned him a nickname. What was it?

1. Who was the 'Iron Chancellor' who united Germany?

2. Which Roman emperor sentenced St Peter to crucifixion?

3. Name the German mayor of West Berlin who became internationally known during the Berlin Wall crisis.

12. Mohandas Gandhi was born in India and studied law in England. Where did he practise law before returning to India in 1914?

13. Why did Vorster resign from the presidency of South Africa?

14. What was formally announced by George Bush and Mikhail Gorbachev on 3 December 1989?

15. Which Christian democrat politician was imprisoned by Hitler but later became Chancellor of Germany?

16. Who successfully led North Vietnam in the Vietnam War?

17. Which king ordered the construction of the Tower of London?

18. Name the Chinese leader who organized the Long March beginning in 1934.

19. Lech Walesa founded Solidarity in Poland and later became President. Originally he was a trade union leader but what was his trade?

20. Who was given the title 'Emperor of the West' at his coronation in Rome in AD800?

21. Where was US diplomat Henry Kissinger born?

22. Where was British Prime Minister Winston Churchill born?

23. Who became President of Romania in 1990?

24. Hastings Banda became the first President of which country in 1966?

25. Who succeeded Juan Perón in Argentina in 1974?

Q 13

1. To which family of fish does the char belong?

2. In fishing, lines, hooks, floats and weights are known collectively as what?

3. Where would you find clownfish, boxfish and lion fish?

4. Which TV private eye enjoyed fishing with his father?

5. For what type of fishing are waggler floats used?

6. What are spade end, tucked half blood and dropper loop?

7. Are fish equipped with eyelids?

8. Why should tunny fish be cooked soon after capture?

9. What tool would an angler use to lift a hooked fish from the water?

10. How would an angler keep his catch alive?

11. Salmon return to the river where they were spawned to lay their eggs in fresh water. How do they identify the right river?

12. What type of fish is a jack?

13. What are 'Thunder & Lightning', 'Wycombe's Fancy' and 'Greenwell's Glory'?

14. Which fish has black spots which are said to represent the finger marks of St Peter?

15. For fishing from the beach you need a powerful rod which can cast long distances. What is it called?

16. Name the type of bait which fishermen dig up on sand or mud beaches, where it can be identified by casts.

17. At what time of year does the rainbow trout spawn?

18. Flying fish swim just below the surface then when danger approaches they fly over the water using outspread pectorals as wings. What gives them the power for flight?

19. Which are the only fish in which the head forms a right-angle with the body?

20. Where does the sturgeon breed?

21. Barbels are essential to catfish. What are they?

22. What are large whites, pinkies and squatts?

23. Which type of fishing was featured in the film *A River Runs Through It*?

24. What is the largest of the flatfish?

25. Which fish camouflage themselves on the seabed by remaining still and trusting to their sandy colouring?

Q15

1. What is the plural of mongoose?

2. Which Jerusalem church marks the spot where Joseph of Arimathea buried Jesus?

3. Which river flows through the city of Limerick in Ireland?

4. Why do seals appear to cry?

5. Which game was named after the Duke of Beaufort's house in Gloucestershire, England?

6. Who made the song 'My Old Dutch' famous?

7. What is pumpernickel?

8. If you were visiting the 'Met' in New York, where would you be going?

9. What mysterious trade was carried on at Jamaica Inn?

10. Which European country's flag is a yellow cross on a blue field?

11. During which two centuries did Queen Elizabeth I reign?

12. In falconry, what is a stoop?

13. Where would a troglodyte live?

14. In what would a cryptologist specialize?

15. What is the capital of Venezuela?

16. Which planet is closest to the sun?

17. Who wrote the 'New World' symphony?

18. In the television series *Mission Impossible*, what did the initials IMF stand for?

19. What would you be doing if you were wearing a tutu?

20. Which legendary character has been portrayed by both Sean Connery and his son Jason?

21. Who asked for the head of John the Baptist, according to the Bible story?

22. In what field is the Brazilian Jorge Amado well known?

23. Which words appear on the George Cross?

24. What song became a hit single after Lee Marvin sang it in *Paint Your Wagon*?

25. Are dates, pomegranates and avocados tropical or subtropical fruits?

Geography and Travel • City Sites

1. Barcelona
2. Brandenburg Gate
3. Lac Léman
4. Milan
5. Both used to be markets
6. Stockholm
7. Alcatraz
8. Amsterdam
9. In the complex of the Grand Palace
10. Munich
11. Tiananmen Square
12. O'Connell Street
13. Doric
14. Montmartre
15. Trevi
16. Agra
17. Shanghai
18. A skating rink
19. Hong Kong
20. Brussels' oldest citizen
21. Rome
22. Sydney Opera house
23. Jerusalem
24. Florian
25. Guggenheim

Popular Culture • Jazz

1. Satchelmouth
2. The Creole Jazz Band
3. The first white jazz musician
4. Stride piano
5. Ferdinand Joseph Lemott
6. Benny Goodman
7. Wynton and Branford
8. Lionel Hampton
9. Jazz funk
10. Billie Holiday
11. Moonlight Serenade
12. Drums
13. New Orleans
14. Django Reinhardt
15. Violin
16. Huddie Ledbetter
17. Bebop
18. Miles Davis
19. 13 or more
20. Saxophone
21. Boogie woogie
22. Duke Ellington
23. Cornet, trombone and clarinet
24. Coleman Hawkins
25. Cool jazz

Indoors and Out • Trees and Shrubs

1. A small, edible nut
2. The Romans
3. The flowers attract bees and insects
4. Creamy-white, bell-shaped flowers
5. Heart wood
6. Purple and bronze
7. Deciduous
8. Sugar maple
9. It has strawberry-like, but tasteless fruits
10. The pea family (*Leguminosae*)
11. The cherry
12. It throws up suckers
13. Pinkish-purple
14. Californian redwood (*Sequoia sempervirens*)
15. The silkworm
16. The seeds are spread by the wind
17. New Zealand
18. Heart-shaped
19. They have a single stem, grown at an angle to form a hedge, with no large spreading branches
20. Firethorn
21. Azaleas
22. Eucalyptus
23. Cypress
24. Hawthorn
25. Cedar

Past and Present • Modern Technology

1. Eight
2. Random Access Memory
3. 1970s
4. IBM
5. Dot-matrix printer
6. Bar code
7. Egypt
8. Telstar
9. Computer languages
10. 1970s
11. Optical fibres
12. One million floating operations per second
13. C-3PO and R2-D2
14. Personal identity number
15. A mouse
16. Modem
17. Read-only memory
18. 1980s
19. Facsimile
20. Musical keyboard
21. Produces a regular timing signal
22. Slave labour
23. Send messages back to the TV station
24. Computer aided design
25. A standard keyboard

Youth World • Cartoons

1. Sylvester
2. 'What's up Doc?'
3. For their violence
4. Felix
5. Bedrock
6. Beagle
7. Popeye
8. Scrooge McDuck
9. Ronald Searle
10. Leonard Nimoy
11. *Plane crazy*
12. He is short-sighted
13. Betty Boop
14. William Hanna and Joseph Barbera
15. Speedy Gonzales
16. Asterix
17. Roadrunner
18. Chip has one tooth, Dale has two
19. Bloodhound
20. The Island of Sweetwater
21. Phileas Fogg
22. 60
23. Jessica
24. Bugs Bunny
25. Fred and Wilma

Famous Folk • Statesmen and Tyrants

1. Bismarck
2. Nero
3. Willy Brandt
4. Idi Amin
5. Michael Manley
6. François Duvalier
7. U Thant
8. Jawaharla Nehru
9. Suicide
10. Ewart
11. Ivan the Terrible
12. South Africa
13. Financial scandal
14. End of the Cold War
15. Konrad Adenauer
16. Ho Chi Minh
17. William the Conqueror
18. Mao Tse-tung
19. Electrician
20. Charlemagne
21. Bavaria, Germany
22. Blenheim Palace
23. Ion Iliescu
24. Malawi
25. Isabel Perón

Sport and Leisure • Fish and Fishing

1. Salmonidae
2. Tackle
3. On a coral reef
4. James Rockford
5. Stillwater fishing
6. Types of knot
7. No, their eyes do not close
8. They are prone to a type of bacterial decay which can render them poisonous
9. A landing net
10. By using a keep-net
11. By smell
12. Pike
13. Flies used in Fly-fishing
14. John Dory
15. Beachcaster
16. Lugworms
17. Spring
18. The action of the tail
19. Seahorses
20. Rivers
21. Whiskers
22. Maggots
23. Fly fishing
24. Halibut
25. Rays

Pot Luck

1. Mongooses
2. Church of the Holy Sepulchre
3. River Shannon
4. They produce tears to keep their eyes moist
5. Badminton
6. Albert Chevalier
7. A type of black bread
8. Metropolitan Opera House
9. Smuggling
10. Sweden
11. 16th and 17th
12. The falcon's dive on its prey
13. In a cave
14. Cracking codes
15. Caracas
16. Mercury
17. Dvořák
18. Impossible Missions Force
19. Ballet dancing
20. Robin Hood
21. Salome
22. Novel writing
23. 'For gallantry'
24. Wandrin' Star
25. Subtropical

1. At what age does a baby kangaroo, or joey, leave its mother's pouch because it has grown too big?

2. Which animals have species known as Burchell's and Grevy's?

3. Where is the calf of the hippopotamus born?

4. Gorillas and chimpanzees are found in Africa. In which continent would you find gibbons and orang-utans?

5. From which country did the pheasant originate?

6. The kinkajou has acquired a popular name because of its fondness for a certain type of food. What is the name?

7. How does the skunk keep enemies at bay?

8. Which is the only type of deer to have been domesticated, so that it supplies meat, milk and skins?

9. How many chambers has the stomach of a giraffe?

10. What is unusual about the incubation of the emu's eggs?

11. Some porcupines nest in trees. True or false?

12. Why are bush-babies so called?

13. What type of animal is an impala?

14. The feet of the puffin are red in summer. What colour are they in winter?

15. What does the raccoon seem to do with its food before it eats?

16. Which is the only mammal able to kneel on all fours?

17. What is the name given to the nesting site of penguins?

18. Whales live in groups of 20 to 50. What are the groups called?

19. In which country can wild budgerigars be found?

20. Name the animals popularly thought to commit mass suicide by hurling themselves into the sea.

21. Which is the largest of the American big cats?

22. What is stored in the camel's hump?

23. The roadrunner, found in the stony deserts of North America, is a member of which bird family?

24. Which animal has species called elephant, crabeater and fur?

25. Why do desert-living gerbils never need to drink?

1. Which newspaper was nicknamed 'The Thunderer'?

2. Spiderman's alter ego was newspaper photographer Peter Parker. For which paper did he work?

3. Newspaper reporters now put their copy straight onto a VDU. What do the initials stand for?

4. *Le Figaro* is published in Paris. Is it daily or weekly?

5. Which magazine was launched by Helen Gurley Brown?

6. Canada's first newspaper was the *Halifax Gazette*. In which century was the earliest edition published?

7. The film *Citizen Kane*, starring Orson Welles, was loosely based on the life of which newspaper magnate?

8. Which is larger, a tabloid or a broadsheet newspaper?

9. Name the Australian businessman who has made a fortune in the newspaper industry.

10. Was *Vogue* first published in America in 1892, 1905 or 1921?

11. Which is Britain's oldest Sunday newspaper?

12. What newspaper do the Flintstones read?

13. In a newspaper, what is a 'splash'?

14. Reporter Clark Kent worked for the *Daily Planet*. By what name was he better known?

15. New York's penny paper was launched in 1833 and had the same name as a current British tabloid. What was it?

16. Which magazine has a yellow border on the front cover?

17. In which decade was *Marie Claire* first published in France?

18. For which newspaper did TV's Lou Grant work?

19. *Der Spiegel* is a famous German publication. What does the name mean in English?

20. Which newspaper had almost 950 pages one morning in October 1965?

21. Woodward and Bernstein wrote for which newspaper?

22. How often is *Life* magazine published?

23. Newspaper proprietor Max Aitken was born in Canada in 1879. By what name is he better known?

24. *Barrons* is a well-respected weekly publication in the US. What field does it cover?

25. The wife of disgraced tycoon Robert Maxwell published her autobiography in 1994. What is her name?

Q 18

6. What is added to stock to make Venetian soup?

7. Which type of meat is traditionally used in moussaka?

8. When barbecuing meat, how would you flavour and tenderize it in advance?

9. What is the traditional material used for a wok?

10. In a freezer kept at −18°C (0°F), how long can you store sausages?

11. In a freezer kept at −18°C (0°F), which could you keep longer, beef or pork?

12. Which type of cheeses are Liptauer, Feta and Munster?

13. What would you add to béchamel sauce to make aurore sauce?

14. At a meal with several courses, when would you serve Welsh rarebit?

15. American recipes give quantities of ingredients in standard cups. How much sugar (caster or granulated) does one cup hold?

16. When making cappuccino you would use a fine ground coffee. What kind would you use in a percolator?

17. What are riccini, bucatini and ziti?

1. What is the substance that gels in water and enables jam to set?

2. Goulash takes its name from the Hungarian word for shepherd. What spice gives goulash its distinctive flavour?

3. In microwave cooking, what is the other name for standing time, when the food can continue cooking after it leaves the oven?

4. What name is given to bread dipped in beaten egg and fried?

5. The Italian pasta called tagliatelle comes in what shape?

18. In what type of oven are pizzas traditionally made?

19. If you were serving an Indian 'thali', how would you present it?

20. Which of these materials would be suitable for use in microwaves: glass, ceramics, metal, paper?

21. If you were making a bisque, what main ingredient would you use?

22. What is 'beurre fondu'?

23. What is the zest of an orange or lemon?

24. What is the traditional herbal accompaniment for lamb?

25. If a recipe called for 450g (1lb) butter, what would be the equivalent in American cups?

Q 11

1. When the state of Israel was first formed, which country occupied the West Bank?

2. Lawrence of Arabia helped to organize Arab revolt against whose rule?

3. In which war did Israel defeat the Arab nations in June 1967?

4. Which Egyptian leader nationalized the Suez Canal in 1956?

5. After World War II a million Jews were in DP camps across Europe. What did DP stand for?

6. Which Egyptian king was forced to abdicate after the army coup in 1952?

7. Where did Black September terrorists kill 11 Israeli athletes in 1972?

8. Who was Israel's leader at the time of the Yom Kippur war?

9. The Gulf War between Iran and Iraq began in 1980. When did it end?

10. Which was the only Arab state to support Iran against Iraq?

11. What did Saddam Hussein abolish in Iraq in 1977?

12. When Iraqi forces invaded Kuwait in 1990 the ruler and the Crown Prince fled. Where did they take refuge?

13. At the beginning of the Gulf War, Saddam Hussein detained western hostages in Iraq, keeping many of them at military targets. What was this policy called?

14. Against which nations did Saddam Hussein fire Scud missiles when the Allies attacked in the Gulf war?

15. Who has been leader of the PLO since 1969?

16. What percentage of the world's oil reserves is owned by Saudi Arabia?

17. Who was the first prime minister of the independent state of Israel?

18. What name was given to the operation to liberate Kuwait from Iraqi invaders?

19. The Kurds in the north of Iraq openly rebelled against Saddam Hussein. When government troops hit back, where did Kurdish refugees gather?

20. What council was formed by Iraq, Jordan, North Yemen and Egypt in 1989?

21. Since 1984 there has been guerilla fighting in what part of Turkey?

22. The Palestinian Al Fatah was formed as an illicit organization in 1956. Al Fatah is Arabic for what?

23. Hafiz Al-Assad has been president of which country since 1971?

24. What was the name given to the popular Palestinian uprising against Israeli occupation?

25. At the 1991 Madrid peace conference Hanan Ashrawi, a professor of English literature and a Christian, was the unlikely spokesperson for which organisation?

7. In Italy, who would study at the Instituto Magistrale?

8. What is the French baccalauréat?

9. Many Australian children live in the outback, too isolated to attend school. They talk to teachers by two-way radio and submit work by post. What is the 'school' called?

10. Which school did Billy Bunter attend?

11. Arnold Schwarzenegger plays a policeman masquerading as a teacher in which film?

1. To which creature does Shakespeare compare the schoolboy in the famous 'Ages of Man' speech?

2. In America, what is a sophomore?

3. What is a magnet school?

4. How many key stages are there in the British national curriculum?

5. Which schoolboy did Flashman bully in a famous novel?

6. A fraternity is a society of male college students in America. What is the female equivalent?

12. In Germany, what are Fachschulen?

13. What is TEFL teaching?

14. Plato was the pupil of which famous teacher?

15. Plato was the teacher of which famous pupil?

16. What is the main difference between British and American public schools?

17. The University of Paris is normally known by the name of one of its departments. What is it?

18. Which teacher taught Helen Keller to communicate?

19. King Hussein of Jordan was educated at which British public school?

20. *Blackboard Jungle* is a classic film of a tough urban school, based on a novel by which author?

21. What is the name of the school in Charles Dickens' *Nicholas Nickelby*?

22. The word education is based on the Latin educo. What does it mean?

23. In which field of education did Maria Montessori introduce revolutionary ideas?

24. What is the name usually given to the older, more traditional universities of the north-eastern US?

25. Bel Kaufman's bestseller about a New York public school was filmed as *Up the Down Staircase*. Who starred as the new teacher?

Q 5

Q 10

1. Who was known as the 'King of Marches'?

2. Sir Thomas Beecham founded two orchestras. The first was the London Philharmonic in 1932. What was the other?

3. Which modern American musician wrote the ballets *Billy the Kid*, *Rodeo* and *Appalachian Spring*?

4. Who wrote the score for the film *Lawrence of Arabia*?

5. Before James Galway embarked on a freelance career, he was a flautist with which orchestra?

6. What name is given to the music associated with Debussy, Ravel and Delius?

7. How old was Johann Strauss when he wrote his first waltz?

8. Which opera, the story of ill-fated love, was written by George Gershwin for a black cast in 1935?

9. What nationality was Anton Bruckner?

10. From what handicap did J. S. Bach suffer in later life?

11. What forced Rachmaninov to leave his native country?

12. The oratorio *The Dream of Gerontius* was first performed in Germany in 1901. Who was the composer?

13. What nationality was Gustav Holst?

14. Name the Beatles' manager who died in 1967.

15. Which composer always began his score with the words 'In nomine Domini' and ended it with 'Laus Deo'?

16. Whose musical shows include *Kiss me Kate* and *The Gay Divorcee*?

17. Rimsky-Korsakov was a leading member of a Russian group called what?

18. At the age of six Mozart was touring Europe as a performer with his talented older sister. What was her name?

19. Which composer founded the Festival Theatre in Bayreuth?

20. Who was the first great master of the string quartet?

21. For which English king did Handel write his *Water Music* in 1717?

22. What nationality was Jean Sibelius?

23. At what age did Chopin make his debut as a pianist?

24. Frederick Delius was born in England but in 1884 he went to Florida. What business was he engaged in?

25. Wagner's *Ring of the Nibelung* consists of four epic music dramas. Which is the first?

Q 14

1. What does the Jewish festival of the Passover commemorate?

2. During Ramadan, in the ninth month of the Muslim year, what is observed during daylight hours?

3. When does the famous Mardi Gras carnival in New Orleans take place?

4. In the Christian calendar, advent is a period of preparation for which festival?

5. Wesak is an important festival for Buddhists. What does it mark?

Q 3

6. Which country has a Boys' Festival, or Childrens' Day, on 5 May, when paper carp are hoisted on to poles?

7. Holi is a harvest time festival for Hindus when people light bonfires and throw coloured water over one another. Which deity does it honour?

8. During the pilgrimage to Mecca, male pilgrims don what type of dress?

9. Which celebration, once linked with dancing and flowers and now associated with socialism, was forbidden in England in the time of Oliver Cromwell?

10. In Thailand Songkrar Day is also New Year. What is the main feature of the celebrations, held on 31 December?

11. The Muslim Hijrat commemorates whose journey from Mecca to Medina?

12. The Jewish Hanukkah celebrates the recapture and rededication of the Temple of Jerusalem in 165BC. It lasts eight days; what happens on each day?

13. When is Thanksgiving celebrated in the US?

14. At the Chinese New Year, people honour the kitchen god, who will then report back to heaven on their conduct. What kind of dance is associated with the festivities?

15. For Christians, Lent means the 40 days leading up to Easter. What day marks the beginning of Lent?

16. What does the Jewish feast Shavout celebrate?

17. The first Christians did not observe Christmas, but it was being celebrated by which century?

18. Which Hindu festival of lights, when lights stand in every window, honours Lakshmi, the goddess of fortune?

19. Who do the Chinese particularly remember at Ching Ming?

20. Which saint's feast day falls on 26 December in the Christian calendar?

21. In many European and Asian countries, on which day do people play tricks on one another?

22. What does Rosh Hashanah mark for the Jews?

23. Which religion celebrates Baisakhi?

24. In which German town does the famous Oktoberfest, where beer flows freely, take place?

25. Name the ancient Celtic celebration, particularly popular in the US, which marks the time when witches and evil spirits were supposed to be driven away before the beginning of the new year.

1. What are baby squirrels called?

2. Which chain of shops was originally called the Great Five Cent Store?

3. What is measured by a chronometer?

4. Which aviator made the first solo Trans-Atlantic flight?

5. In the nursery rhyme, what did the dish run away with?

6. Name the capital of New Zealand.

7. What is gymnophobia?

8. Who painted *The Rake's Progress?*

9. In the TV series *Dempsey and Makepeace*, was Dempsey or Makepeace the man?

10. What kind of creature is a flying dragon?

11. Whose life is portrayed in the musical *Evita*?

12. Which is the world's largest freshwater lake?

13. What is the main ingredient of taramasalata?

14. In which film did Charlie Chaplin first speak on screen?

15. If you were suffering from gingivitis, what part of your body would be affected?

16. What is the main explosive ingredient of dynamite?

17. If a golfer loses a ball, what is the penalty?

18. In Shakespeare's *Macbeth*, which king is killed in his sleep?

19. What is the meaning of the word 'karate'?

20. Three of the four largest deserts in the world are the Sahara, Arabian and Australian. What is the fourth?

21. According to George Orwell, who is watching us?

22. How many dimes are there in one American dollar?

23. Name the character who sings 'I Feel Pretty' in *West Side Story*.

24. In which operetta would you find Yum-Yum and Nanki-Poo?

25. What did the nickname 'dinkies' describe when applied to a couple?

Answers to Quiz 2

Geography and Travel • Wildlife

1. Six months
2. The zebra
3. Under water
4. Asia
5. China
6. Honey bear
7. It sprays a smelly liquid which can cause a predator temporary blindness
8. Reindeer
9. Four
10. The male sits on the

eggs, not the female
11. True
12. Because their cry sounds like a wailing baby
13. Antelope
14. Yellow
15. It washes the food
16. The elephant
17. Rookery
18. Pods
19. Australia
20. Lemmings

21. The jaguar
22. Fat
23. Cuckoo
24. Seal
25. They obtain the moisture they need from the overnight dew on their food

Youth World • Education

1. A snail
2. A second-year student in high school or college
3. It specializes in a particular area of the curriculum
4. Four
5. Tom Brown
6. Sorority
7. Teachers
8. School leaving certificate

9. School of the Air
10. Greyfriars
11. *Kindergarten Cop*
12. Technical colleges
13. Teaching English as a foreign language
14. Socrates
15. Aristotle
16. In the US they are free: in Britain they are fee-paying
17. Sorbonne
18. Anne Sullivan

19. Harrow
20. Evan Hunter
21. Dotheboys Hall
22. To draw out
23. Infant teaching
24. Ivy League
25. Sandy Dennis

Popular Culture • Newspapers and Magazines

1. *The Times*
2. The *Daily Bugle*
3. Visual display unit
4. Daily
5. *Cosmopolitan*
6. 18th century
7. William Randolph Hearst
8. Broadsheet
9. Rupert Murdoch
10. 1892
11. The *Observer*
12. The *Daily Slate*

13. A front-page lead story
14. Superman
15. The *Sun*
16. *National Geographic*
17. 1950s
18. *Los Angeles Tribune*
19. *The Mirror*
20. *New York Times*
21. The *Washington Post*
22. Monthly
23. Lord Beaverbrook
24. Finance
25. Elizabeth

Famous Folk • Musicians and Composers

1. John Philip Sousa
2. Royal Philharmonic, 1947
3. Aaron Copland
4. Maurice Jarre
5. Berlin Philharmonic
6. Impressionist
7. Six
8. *Porgy and Bess*
9. Austrian
10. Blindness
11. The Russian Revolution
12. Elgar

13. English
14. Brian Epstein
15. Haydn
16. Cole Porter
17. The Five
18. Anna or Nannerl
19. Wagner
20. Haydn
21. George I
22. Finnish
23. Eight
24. Orange-growing
25. The Rhinegold (Das

Rheingold)

Indoors and Out • Cookery Course

1. Pectin
2. Paprika
3. Carry over cooking
4. French toast or 'eggy bread'
5. Long ribbons
6. Egg and lemon
7. Lamb
8. Marinade
9. Iron
10. Three months
11. Beef
12. Soft cheeses

13. Tomato
14. The end of the meal
15. 200g (7oz)
16. Medium grind
17. Types of pasta
18. Brick
19. With each dish in a separate small bowl
20. Glass, ceramics, paper
21. Shellfish
22. Butter melted with lemon juice, salt and white pepper

23. The very outside of the peel
24. Mint
25. Two cups

Sport and Leisure • Religious Festivals

1. The escape from slavery in Egypt
2. A strict fast
3. Shrove Tuesday
4. Christmas
5. Buddha's birth, enlightenment and death
6. Japan
7. Krishna
8. A white sheet
9. May Day
10. A water festival

11. Muhammad
12. A new candle is lit on the menorah
13. The fourth Thursday of November
14. Lion dance
15. Ash Wednesday
16. The giving of the Ten Commandments on Mount Sinai
17. Fourth century
18. Diwali
19. The dead

20. St Stephen
21. 1st April, All Fools Day
22. New Year
23. Sikh
24. Munich
25. Hallowe'en

Past and Present • Middle East

1. Jordan
2. Turks
3. Six Day War
4. Nasser
5. Displaced Persons
6. King Farouk
7. Munich Olympics
8. Golda Meir
9. 1988
10. Syria
11. The use of surnames
12. Saudi Arabia
13. The 'human shield

policy'
14. Israel and Saudi Arabia
15. Yasser Arafat
16. 40%
17. David Ben-Gurion
18. Operation Desert Storm
19. On the Turkish border
20. Arab Co-operation Council
21. Kurdistan
22. Victory
23. Syria
24. Intifada

25. PLO

Pot Luck

1. Kittens
2. Woolworths
3. Time
4. Charles Lindbergh
5. Spoon
6. Wellington
7. Fear of nakedness
8. Hogarth
9. Dempsey
10. Lizard
11. Eva Perón
12. Lake Superior
13. Cod's roe

14. *The Great Dictator*
15. Gums
16. Nitro-glycerine
17. One stroke added to the score
18. Duncan
19. Empty hand
20. Gobi
21. Big Brother
22. Ten
23. Maria
24. *The Mikado*
25. Dual income and no

kids

1. In which area of the US would you find a multitude of covered bridges?

2. Lake Tahoe, the largest alpine lake in North America, is half in California and half in which other state?

3. Which is the largest Indian reservation in America?

4. What is the legal drinking age in all American states?

5. In which Canadian town, nicknamed Cowtown, does a famous 'stampede' take place in July each year?

6. Which American city has the largest cruise ship port in the world?

7. A quarter of the world's geysers are found in which national park in Wyoming ?

8. Name the string of islands at the southern tip of Florida.

9. What is the state bird of Texas?

10. In Washington DC, which park is overlooked by the White House?

11. Which mountain range stretches from Alaska to New Mexico?

Q12

12. The Golden Gate Bridge is one of the longest suspension bridges in the world. Which US city does it connect with Marin County?

13. Which capital city stands on Vancouver Island in Canada?

14. In which American state would you find the world's most active volcano?

15. Nearly half the population of Alaska lives in one town. What is its name?

16. Canada's most popular resort stands in its oldest national park. What is its name?

17. The Yukon Territory is named after the Yukon River ('yukon' means 'clear water'). Is it in Canada or the USA?

18. Which American state is known as the Lone Star state?

19. The Pennsylvanian Dutch Country is home to the Amish and Mennonite people, who turn their back on much of the modern world. What nationality were the original immigrants?

20. In which state would you find Carlsbad Caverns, El Morro National Monument and Taos?

21. Which country gave the Statue of Liberty to America?

22. The famous two-week siege of the Alamo, Texas, took place in 1836 when its 187 defenders died. Which country's army besieged the fort?

23. What notable feature would you expect to find at the Mesa Verde National Park in Colorado?

24. Which is the only Canadian province where the urban population is more than 80% of the total?

25. How long is the Grand Canyon?

BOND BOOKS AND FILMS

1. How did James Bond like his martini?

2. Which was the first book to feature James Bond?

3. Who sang the theme song to *A View to a Kill*?

4. Name the producer of the Bond films.

5. Which Bond film features the Carnival at Rio?

6. Who is the villain in *Diamonds are Forever*?

7. In 1973 Roger Moore took over as Bond, but one film tempted Sean Connery back to the role. Which was it?

8. Ursula Andress collects shells on the beach in which film?

9. 'M' is Bond's boss, but who supplies him with his high-tech gadgetry?

10. Which film used Phang Nga Bay, in southern Thailand, as the location for the villain's private island?

11. In the 17th Bond film, *Goldeneye*, who plays Bond's female boss?

12. Which villain likes to bite his victim to death?

13. Which of the Bond girls shares a surname with the secret agent?

14. Who wrote the Bond novels?

15. The film *Casino Royale*, made in 1967, is a spoof. Who plays Bond?

16. Following the death of Bond's creator, who wrote sequels called *Icebreaker*, *Roll of Honour* and *Scorpius*?

17. Pussy Galore runs a 'flying circus' in which film?

18. Who is Mr Big's sidekick in *Live and Let Die*?

19. In which film does George Lazenby play Bond?

20. Which well-known novelist wrote *The James Bond Dossier* in 1965?

21. Who plays the tarot-reading Solitaire in *Live and Let Die*?

22. Matt Munro sang the title song for which film?

23. Which actor appears as Bond for the first time in *The Living Daylights*?

24. In which film does a Lotus car convert into an underwater craft?

25. In *Goldfinger*, what does Oddjob use as a lethal weapon?

1. Apricots are native to which country?

2. The boysenberry was raised in California in the 1930s by Rudolph Boysen. It is thought to come from a mixture of which fruits?

3. What is a 'maiden' fruit tree?

4. Morello is a sour type of which fruit?

5. A date palm has a life of about 80 years. What is the world's most popular variety of date?

6. Which 15th-century explorer brought the pineapple, a native of Brazil, to Spain?

7. Viticulture is the name given to the growing of which fruit?

8. The French are not great gooseberry eaters, except as a basis for a sauce for a fish dish named *groseille à maquereau*. Which fish does it complement?

9. The commercial cultivation of grapefruit began in the 1880s. Where was this?

10. Which type of melon has a yellow-orange skin with green rib markings in a network pattern?

11. What is another name for the papaya or tree melon?

12. Pectin is essential for jam-making. Which will contain more pectin: slightly under-ripe, ripe or slightly over-ripe fruit?

Q6

13. Which fruit has the botanical name *Ribes nigrum*?

14. Apples were cultivated by the ancient Greeks. True or false?

15. Which fruit did a companion of Captain Cook, in north Queensland, describe as a 'kind of wild Plantain, whose fruit was so full of stones that it was scarcely eatable'?

16. When thawing fruit, is it best to thaw it in the fridge or at room temperature?

17. Which Spanish city is thought to have been named after the pomegranate?

18. The durian fruit, native to Malaysia, is notorious for what?

19. Seckle, Jargonelle and Doyenne du Comice are varieties of what type of fruit?

20. The name 'strawberry' is often thought to come from the growers' habit of laying straw round the plants. In fact, it probably comes from what habit of the plant itself?

21. Where was the kiwi fruit first grown and harvested?

22. Which country grows the largest number of mangoes?

23. The carob, a member of the pea family, can be used to replace which substance in cooking?

24. The blackberry, or bramble, belongs to which family of plants?

25. Cranberries are cultivated on a large scale in the eastern US. In what kind of ground are they grown?

4. Christopher Columbus set out to find a route to Asia in 1492. Where did he land?

5. Who created the Moghul empire in India in the 16th century?

6. Which all-male theatre with a highly stylized form was established in Japan in 1586 and can still be seen today?

7. The Spanish adventurer Cortés landed in Mexico in 1518 and by 1521 had conquered the country. Which empire did he destroy in the process?

8. Sebastian Cabot was supported by King Henry VII of England in his explorations and in 1497 discovered Newfoundland. What nationality was he?

9. Europeans who tried to trade with China in the 16th century were not welcomed. Which famous dynasty was at the height of its power?

10. The Julian calendar was used in Europe until the 1580s. Which calendar was adopted after 1582 in Roman Catholic countries and later in Protestant countries?

11. The Renaissance was a great cultural revival in Europe after the Middle Ages. What does 'renaissance' mean?

12. Which Renaissance artist painted the ceiling of the Sistine Chapel and designed the dome of St Peter's in Rome?

1. Which European country was the first to start building its overseas empire?

2. In 1454 the German Johann Gutenberg set up his printing press. Later, he used metal type, but what material did he use to begin with?

3. Which ocean was named by navigator Ferdinand Magellan?

13. In which decade of the 16th century did John Hawkins begin the slave trade by shipping Africans to the West Indies?

14. Which country was discovered by Abel Tasman in 1662 and surveyed by Captain Cook in 1769?

15. What important navigational aid did Flemish geographer Gerardus Mercator produce in 1569?

16. The 16th century was Spain's golden age. Philip II made which city Spain's capital?

17. In 1608 Samuel de Champlain founded the city that was to become Quebec. What trade did he organize between France and Canada?

18. In 1587 Sir Francis Drake destroyed Spanish ships in Cadiz harbour. What did he call this enterprise?

19. The defeat of the Spanish Armada began Spain's decline. What is Drake popularly supposed to have been doing when the Armada was sighted?

20. Which vegetable did Sir Walter Raleigh bring back from his journey to America?

21. In 1488 Bartholomeu Diaz sailed to the southern tip of the African continent and turned back because of bad weather. He called the area the 'Cape of Storms'. What cheery name does it bear today?

22. Which empire was destroyed by Francisco Pizzaro and his forces in the mountains of South America in the 1530s?

23. What name was given to the movement whereby half Europe broke away from the Roman Catholic church and Protestantism flourished?

24. Who succeeded Queen Elizabeth I to the throne of England in 1603?

25. America's first university was founded in 1636 in Cambridge, Massachusetts. Name it.

1. The Sherpas of the Himalayas have always believed that which creature lives beyond the snowline?

2. Which historical figure is supposed to have been the prototype of Bram Stoker's creation *Dracula*?

3. Which ugly, misshapen creatures, in the form of men, are said to lurk in the northern forests of Scandinavia?

4. What type of monsters were defeated by Ragnar of Denmark, Beowulf and St George?

5. Name the imaginary creature described by Lewis Carroll as having 'jaws that bite and claws that catch'.

6. The Marvel comics introduced many monsters, among them the fearsome King of the Negative Zone. What was he aptly named?

7. A werewolf could only be killed by what type of bullet?

8. Which monster appears as Harry in *Harry and the Hendersons*?

9. In the film *Jason and the Argonauts* monsters such as winged harpies and fighting skeletons were produced by a process called 'dynamism' by their creator. Who is he?

10. A lake demon called Ogapogo is said to inhabit Okanagan Lake in Canada. In which province is the lake?

11. Which people believe that 'whowies' and 'bunyips' existed in the Dreamtime?

12. Who was Dr Jekyll's alter ego?

13. Name the dragon who guarded treasure in *The Hobbit*.

14. Modern sightings of the Loch Ness monster began in the 1930s, but which saint and his followers first saw 'Nessie' in AD 565?

15. 'Nessie' is thought by some people to be the survivor of a species of dinosaur believed extinct for 70 million years. What is the species?

16. In *The Hound of the Baskervilles*, a Dartmoor family is plagued by a phantom hound. Name the author of the novel.

17. The giant Goliath was slain by the boy David in the Bible story. Goliath was a member of which army?

18. The Kraken was a legendary monster, said to be big enough to drag down ships. What type of creature is the Kraken now believed to have been?

19. In the film *Ghostbusters*, a pagan deity calls up a monster who appears in a surprisingly cuddly form. What is it?

20. How was King Kong killed?

21. In Canada, the monster Cadborasaurus has been sighted regularly off the coast of Vancouver. What is its nickname?

22. The Bigfoot is often known by its Native American name. What is it?

23. In Bram Stoker's *Lair of the White Worm*, which lady is the worm's human manifestation?

24. Name the home of the giants visited in *Gulliver's Travels*.

25. In James Herbert's *The Rats*, how did the monster rat differ in appearance from the other monster mutants?

Q 1

5. Jonas Salk's research into viruses produced the first effective vaccine against which crippling disease?

6. James Watson, Frances Crick and Maurice Wilkins were awarded the Nobel Prize for their work in which modern field?

7. Who revolutionized surgery by his discovery of anaesthetics in the 1860s?

8. The German physicist who first used mercury in a thermometer also fixed a scale of temperature that still bears his name. What is it?

9. Which Italian astronomer and physicist invented the astronomical telescope and put forward the Law of Accelerated Motion?

10. In 1903 Russian Konstantin Tsiolkovsky drew up designs for a spaceship powered by what?

11. Marie Curie is one of the few people to be awarded two Nobel prizes. The first was the prize for physics in 1903. Who shared this award with her?

12. A lamp used by miners for the detection of gas still bears the name of its inventor. What is it?

13. Edward Jenner developed a vaccination to prevent which disease?

14. Alfred Nobel left the lion's share of his fortune to found the prize that bears his name. He had made his money from which invention?

1. Stephen Hawking, who is confined to a wheelchair and talks with the aid of computers, is best known for his study of what?

2. The fall of an apple spurred Newton into considering what?

3. Who is known as the 'father of nuclear physics'?

4. Wallace Carothers invented a strong, light synthetic fibre. What is it called?

15. In the 19th century Michael Faraday was a pioneer in which field?

16. Work on the atomic bomb was carried on in New Mexico under the direction of J. Robert Oppenheimer. What was the project called?

17. Alexander Fleming discovered penicillin. What type of drug is penicillin?

18. Wernher von Braun worked on rocket development in Germany during World War II. What did he work on in America after the war?

19. Archimedes discovered the principle that when a body is immersed in water, the displaced volume of liquid is equal to the weight of the body. Legend has it that he jumped from his bath and ran naked down the street. What was he shouting?

20. In what field are Louis Daguerre, Karl Kleitsch and George Eastman famous names?

21. Name the Scottish engineer who constructed the Caledonian Canal and the Menai Suspension Bridge.

22. What process takes its name from its inventor, Louis Pasteur?

23. In 1927 Le Maître was the first to advance the theory that the universe began with an explosion. What is this theory called?

24. What 'first' did John Logie Baird achieve in 1925?

25. Name the engineer who produced bouncing bombs to breach German dams and 'Tall Boy' and 'Grand Slam' penetration bombs in World War II.

Q 16

4. There are two basic types of organ pipe. What are they?

5. What was the early name for the pianoforte?

6. Which artist painted *The Beggar's Opera* several times in the 18th century?

7. In which part of the world would you find an orchestra called a gamelan?

8. What is a koto?

9. From which family of instruments does the cittern come?

10. Give the common name for aerophones.

11. Give the common name for chordophones.

12. What was founded in 1876 for the purpose of performing Gilbert and Sullivan operettas?

13. A cappella, 'in church style', is what type of song?

14. In whose memory was the Royal Albert Hall opened in 1871?

15. What is the science of sound called?

16. With which instrument was George Formby associated?

17. Bagpipes were known in Roman times. True or false?

1. What is the name given to a boating song, especially the type sung by gondoliers in Venice?

2. Which simple tune, often played by children, is known as 'cutlets waltz' in France and Germany?

3. What instrument did Sir Charles Wheatstone invent in 1824?

18. What name, meaning 'fellowship' in Italian, was given to a society of musicians and poets in Florence around 1600?

19. In which century was the recorder, or English flute, first used?

20. To which family of musical instruments do the cor anglais and bassoon belong?

21. If a chord is played with the notes individually sounded, how is it described?

22. What name is given to a choir that can be divided in two, so that they can 'answer' one another when singing?

23. In what style would a barbershop quartet sing?

24. Which country's music would be played by a sarangi, a tabla or a shanai?

25. In which century were the operas *Norma*, *Otello* and *Lucia di Lammermoor* written?

1. One-upmanship was invented by which author?

2. What is the chemical symbol for lead?

3. Which country is the original home of the balalaika?

4. Who 'packed her trunk and said goodbye to the circus'?

5. What does the Latin term *tempus fugit* mean?

6. *The Naked Civil Servant* was the story of whose life?

7. Which party did Abraham Lincoln lead?

8. If you were prognathous, what facial feature would you have?

9. What would you do with a toque?

10. The four gospels of the *New Testament* appear in which order?

11. What is the capital of New South Wales in Australia?

12. In legend, King Midas had a gift that sounded valuable, but made life impossible. What was it?

13. Which top model did Richard Gere marry?

14. Which partnership wrote the music and lyrics for *The Sound of Music*?

15. Which element has the lowest boiling point?

16. Give the previous name of the country now called Malawi.

17. In what subjects did artist George Stubbs specialize?

18. Who said: 'Patriotism is the last refuge of a scoundrel'?

19. Which is the correct spelling of the following word: accomodate, acommodate or accommodate?

20. What is the name of the frog in *The Muppet Show*?

21. Hermit, spider and blue are types of which creature?

22. In Scotland, in which room of the house would you find a spurtle?

23. Which nation put the 'gang of four' on trial in the 1970s?

Q20

24. Doris Day sang *Secret Love* and *The Black Hills of Dakota* in which film?

25. What name is given to a show involving satirical and topical sketches and songs?

Answers to Quiz 3

Geography and Travel • North America

1. New England
2. Nevada
3. Navajo
4. 21
5. Calgary
6. Miami
7. Yellowstone
8. Florida Keys
9. Mockingbird
10. Lafayette Park
11. Rocky Mountains
12. San Francisco
13. Victoria
14. Hawaii
15. Anchorage
16. Banff
17. Canada
18. Texas
19. German
20. New Mexico
21. France
22. Mexico's
23. Ancient cliff dwellings
24. Ontario
25. 349 km (217 miles)

Popular Culture • Bond Books and Films

1. Shaken, not stirred
2. *Casino Royale*
3. Duran Duran
4. Cubby Broccoli
5. *Moonraker*
6. Blofeld
7. *Never Say Never Again*
8. *Dr No*
9. 'Q'
10. *The Man with the Golden Gun*
11. Dame Judi Dench
12. Jaws
13. Samantha Bond
14. Ian Fleming
15. David Niven
16. John Gardner
17. *Goldfinger*
18. Tee Hee
19. *On Her Majesty's Secret Service*
20. Kingsley Amis
21. Jane Seymour
22. *From Russia with Love*
23. Timothy Dalton
24. *The Spy Who Loved Me*
25. His hat

Indoors and Out • Fruit Harvest

1. China
2. Blackberry, loganberry and raspberry
3. One-year-old
4. Cherry
5. Deglet Noor
6. Columbus
7. Grapes
8. Mackerel
9. Florida
10. Ogen
11. Pawpaw
12. Slightly under-ripe
13. Blackcurrant
14. True
15. Banana
16. In the fridge
17. Granada
18. Its pungent smell
19. Pear
20. Its runners are inclined to 'stray'
21. New Zealand
22. India
23. Chocolate
24. Rose
25. Wet, peaty bogs

Past and Present • The Age of Expansion and Discovery

1. Portugal
2. Wood
3. Pacific
4. West Indies
5. Akbar
6. Kabuki
7. Aztec
8. Italian
9. Ming
10. Gregorian
11. Rebirth
12. Michelangelo
13. 1560s
14. New Zealand
15. A new system of map-making
16. Madrid
17. Fur
18. Singeing the King of Spain's beard
19. Playing bowls
20. Potato
21. Cape of Good Hope
22. Inca
23. The Reformation
24. James I
25. Harvard

Youth World • Monsters

1. Yeti
2. Vlad the Impaler
3. Trolls
4. Dragons
5. The Jabberwocky
6. Annihilus
7. Silver
8. Bigfoot
9. Ray Harryhausen
10. British Columbia
11. The Aborigines of Australia
12. Mr Hyde
13. Smaug
14. St Columba
15. Plesiosaur
16. Conan Doyle
17. Philistines
18. A giant squid
19. A giant marshmallow man
20. He was shot down by aircraft from the Empire State Building
21. Caddy
22. Sasquatch
23. Lady Arabella March
24. Brobdingnag
25. It was white with two heads

Famous Folk • Scientists

1. Black holes
2. The force of gravity
3. Ernest Rutherford
4. Nylon
5. Polio
6. DNA
7. Joseph Lister
8. Fahrenheit
9. Galileo
10. Liquid oxygen and liquid hydrogen
11. She shared it with her brother Pierre
12. Davy
13. Smallpox
14. Gelignite
15. Electricity and magnetism
16. Manhattan Project
17. Antibiotic
18. Space rockets
19. Eureka!
20. Photography
21. Thomas Telford
22. Pasteurization
23. The 'big bang' theory
24. The first television transmitter
25. Barnes Wallis

Sport and Leisure • Making Music

1. Barcarolle
2. Chopsticks
3. Concertina
4. Flue and Reed
5. Fortepiano
6. William Hogarth
7. Indonesia
8. A Japanese form of zither
9. Guitar
10. Wind instruments
11. Stringed instruments
12. D'Oyly Carte Opera Company
13. Unaccompanied
14. Queen Victoria's husband, Prince Albert
15. Acoustics
16. Ukelele
17. True
18. Camerata
19. 12th century
20. The oboe
21. Arpeggio
22. Double choir
23. Close harmony
24. India
25. 19th century

Pot Luck

1. Stephen Potter
2. Pb
3. Russia
4. Nellie the elephant
5. Time flies
6. Quentin Crisp
7. Republican
8. You would have a projecting jaw
9. Wear it
10. Matthew, Mark, Luke, John
11. Sydney
12. Everything he touched turned to gold
13. Cindy Crawford
14. Rogers and Hammerstein
15. Helium
16. Nyasaland
17. Horses
18. Dr Samuel Johnson
19. Accommodate
20. Kermit
21. Crab
22. Kitchen
23. China
24. Calamity Jane
25. Revue

1. Where in the world does the largest car and passenger ferry operate?

2. Steam locomotives need fuel, which is kept in a wagon next to the engine. What is the wagon called?

3. Where was the first elevated railway in the world, in the late 19th century?

4. In London it is the underground, in New York it is the subway. What is it in Paris?

5. Every cargo ship has a Plimsoll line. What is indicated when the water reaches that line?

6. When was the first Channel tunnel begun?

7. In the language of aircraft and flying, what is 'drag'?

8. In which country would you find the high-speed, tilting train called the Pendolino?

9. What is the world's largest airliner?

10. What 'first' in flight did Richard Branson and Per Lindstrand achieve in 1987?

11. Which country opened its first underground railway in 1904?

12. What was invented by Kirkpatrick MacMillan, a Scot, in about 1840?

13. The Blue Riband of the Atlantic, awarded to the liner making the fastest crossing of the Atlantic, was won by the *Queen Mary* on her maiden voyage in 1936. How fast was the crossing?

14. The Isle of Man TT motor-cycle race was established in 1907. What does TT stand for?

15. 'Big Boys', the largest and heaviest locomotives in the world, first appeared in 1941 on which railroad?

16. The *Cutty Sark*, one of the most famous tea clippers, was built in 1869. Where can it now be seen as a museum?

17. The Japanese underground employs burly, uniformed officials with white gloves. What is their job?

18. Murder on the *Orient Express*, the 1974 film starring Albert Finney, was based on whose novel?

19. Who designed the locomotive *Rocket* in 1829?

20. Where did the diesel engine get its name?

21. Which type of boat has underwater wings that develop lift in the water?

22. What was the name of the first nuclear-powered submarine launched by the USA in 1955?

23. Where is the world's steepest 'rack' railway?

24. When were wheeled vehicles first invented?

25. Which English 'character' played the publisher interested in the race to promote aviation in *Those Magnificent Men in their Flying Machines*?

Q 1

1. The modern illustration of Sagittarius is a bowman. How was this sign depicted in early forms of astrology?

2. What is the birthstone for those born under the sign of Leo?

3. Which are the fire signs?

4. According to the Chinese horoscope, 1996 is the year of what animal?

5. If you were born at the end of May, which sign would you belong to?

6. There is a beautiful set of 15th-century images on a famous clocktower in Venice. Where is the clocktower situated?

7. Which element governs the sign of Libra?

8. What zodiacal age are we about to enter, or have just entered?

9. Which sign has amethyst as a birthstone?

10. In early 1995 the Royal Astronomical Society announced that there should be 13 signs rather than 12. What did they call the extra sign?

11. Name the only sign not represented by a living creature.

12. If you were the strong, silent type, solid and steady, sometimes downright obstinate, what sign is most likely to be yours?

13. What are sigils?

14. Which sign do those born on 1 April belong to?

15. The emerald is the birthstone of which sign?

16. The sign of Virgo belongs to which element?

17. Today, Cancer is usually represented by the crab. How was it represented in early astrology?

18. How many signs does the Chinese horoscope have?

19. Pisces is usually represented by two fishes swimming in opposite directions. What is unusual about the fishes in the basilica church of San Miniato al Monte in Florence?

20. Which sign is represented by the goat?

21. Two of the water signs are Cancer and Scorpio. What is the third?

22. In which cathedral is the oldest zodiac in England to be found?

23. In reading the zodiac, what is the 'cusp'?

24. If you are versatile, changeable and impatient, with two sides to

your personality and able to do two things at once, you were probably born under what sign?

25. The 12 divisions of the Zodiac in current use were established by about 500BC. How many signs did the old Babylonian zodiac have?

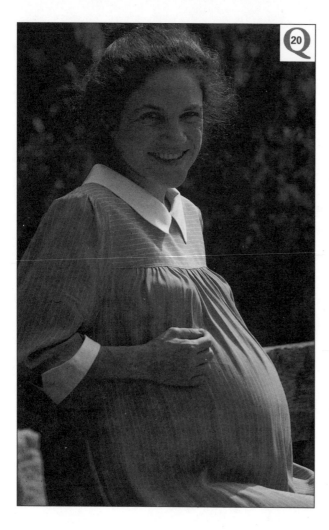

Q20

3. How many amino acids is it essential for children to obtain from food?

4. Insulin controls the amount of sugar in the blood. Which organ produces insulin?

5. What name is given to the use of essential oils on the skin for a wide range of therapeutic effects?

6. Mesomorphs are well-muscled athletic people. What are ectomorphs?

7. What word describes plump people with round heads and pear-shaped bodies?

8. Which organ would a doctor examine with an otoscope?

9. Many people are allergic to tartrazine. What is it?

10. NPT is the length of time skin can stay in the sun without burning. What do the initials stand for?

11. What diet, which triples the average protein intake and cuts fat and carbohydrates, was invented by New York specialist Dr H. Tarnower?

12. Which gland produces the hormones that control the body's metabolism?

13. What would an exfoliating face pack do to your skin?

14. What name is given to the fungus infection that affects the skin between the toes?

1. Which type of fat can increase the cholesterol level in blood?

2. How many amino acids is it essential for adults to obtain from food?

15. Ketosis would result from what inadequacy in the diet?

16. When making up, at what stage should you apply blusher?

17. What is the normal body temperature?

18. The Beverly Hills diet was developed by Judy Mazel in California. What is it based on?

19. Haematology is concerned with which area of medicine?

20. Why is it important that a pregnant woman should not catch rubella?

21. What treatment is based on the idea that there are energy channels in the feet that relate to every organ and function of the body?

22. Many people suffer from dry or oily hair. What is combination hair?

23. A dialysis machine replaces the functioning of which organs?

24. What is the Alexander technique famous for improving as a result of its therapies?

25. Ophthalmology is concerned with which area of the body?

1. Which religious leader looked over the Salt Lake Valley in 1847 and announced 'this is the place'?

2. The Maronites are the largest religious group in the Lebanon. Which religion do they belong to?

3. Who was the religious leader who returned to Iran from exile in 1979 and described the USA as the 'great Satan'?

4. The Guru Granth Sahib, or Adi Granth, is the holy book of which religion?

5. In which country did Buddhism originate?

6. How did Protestantism get its name?

7. For Hindus who is the Supreme Being?

8. Who is the spiritual leader of Tibet, enthroned at the age of five and forced to leave the country after the Chinese invaded?

9. Desmond Tutu is the Anglican archbishop of which South African town?

10. What are the two main Muslim sects?

11. Which faith was founded in the late 1850s by Baha'u'Ullah and is characterized by the absence of priests or public rituals?

12. In what language was the New Testament of the Bible originally written?

13. In which decade were women priests authorized in the USA?

14. Which country did Pope John Paul II visit in early 1995 to receive a rapturous welcome?

15. Which religious group was founded by George Fox in the 17th century?

16. The followers of which religion believe that Haile Selassie of Ethiopia was the Messiah?

17. In Buddhism what is the name given to the final goal of human endeavour?

18. What type of churches are the Elim Church and the Assemblies of God?

19. In Confucianism, the origin of things is seen as the union of which principles?

20. Who was the first Archbishop of Canterbury?

21. Where did the Prophet Muhammad live and die after he fled from Mecca, making it a holy city second only to Mecca?

22. The first five books of the Hebrew Bible are contained in what Jewish holy book?

23. Where did John Bunyan write *Pilgrim's Progress*, about a religious journey through life?

24. William Booth founded the Salvation Army in 1865. To which religious sect did he originally belong?

25. Liberal Judaism goes further than Reform Judaism in trying to adapt the faith to the modern world. What is the other name given to this movement?

1. In what year did Morris and Rose Michtom sell the first teddy bears, named after President Theodore Roosevelt?

2. In which decade of the 20th century did machine-washable teddies appear?

3. Which bear is called 'the Lord of the Arctic'?

4. The name 'koala' comes from the Aboriginal 'no drink'. Why is the koala so called?

5. Where does the koala bear usually sleep?

6. Who wrote about the 'bear of little brain'?

7. Name the teddy bear who is Sebastian Flyte's constant companion in Evelyn Waugh's *Brideshead Revisited*?

8. The only South American bear is the Andean bear, which has white circles round its eyes. What is its popular name?

9. How do bears differ in their eating habits from other carnivores?

10. Name the bear from *The Muppet Show*.

11. The first teddy bear in space orbited the earth in Salyut 6. What was its name?

12. What is the favourite food of the sloth bear, or Indian bear?

13. According to the song, which American hero 'killed him a bear when he was only three'?

14. Who stole the porridge belonging to the three bears?

15. The commonest type of bear is the brown bear. How long do the brown bear cubs stay with their mother?

16. What sport did 'Bear' Bryant coach?

17. Brer Bear is a character in the stories of Uncle Remus, the old cotton-plantation slave. Who wrote the stories?

18. Archibald Ormsby Gore was the much-loved bear of which famous poet?

19. *Bear Island* was a 1980 film starring Donald Sutherland and Vanessa Redgrave. On which author's adventure novel was it based?

20. The sun bear, or Malayan bear, feeds at night. How and where does it spend its days?

21. The grizzly bear, now found mainly in northern Canada, is the north American race of which type of bear?

22. Which fictional bear lived in a bear pit in Berne, Switzerland?

23. What name is given to the hobby of collecting teddy bears?

24. The American black bear is the best known of the black bears. In which month are the cubs usually born?

25. Where did Paddington Bear come from?

73

Q 21

3. Which American chat show hostess appeared in the movie *The Color Purple*?

4. Who became minister and then prime minister?

5. Which English actress stars as a 'medicine woman'?

6. Name the character played by David Hasselhof in *Baywatch*.

7. Who played JFK in *Kennedy*?

8. Kevin Whately plays Sergeant Lewis. Whose trusty sidekick is he?

9. At the beginning of each episode of *Fame*, which actress said: 'You want fame. Well, fame costs and right here's where you start paying'?

10. What type of show is presented by Sally Jessy Raphael, Vanessa and Donahue?

11. Which character is played by Corbin Bernsen in *LA Law*?

12. Name the son of an actor father who patrolled the streets of San Francisco with Karl Malden.

1. Who are Sky, Hawk, Nightshade, Jet and Sabre?

2. Alan Alda won three awards in different categories for *MASH*. What were the categories?

13. In which series does David Jason play an unconventional policeman?

14. Name the first Dr Who.

15. Who has been investigating the private life of plants?

16. Which irascible pensioner is played by Richard Wilson in *One Foot in the Grave*?

17. In *The Buccaneers*, who played the governess, Miss Testvalley?

18. Which actor from *LA Law* joined the precinct in *NYPD Blue* as David Caruso left?

19. Who plays Dr Mark Greene in *ER*?

20. In which store did Miss Brahms, played by Wendy Richard, work?

21. Who starred with Bill Cosby in *I Spy*?

22. In which classic series did Clint Eastwood play Rowdy Yates?

23. Who wrote *Only Victims*, about the activities of the Un-American Activities Committee?

24. Name the playwright husband of actress Maureen Lippman.

25. Which actor played Orry Main in the mini-series *North and South*?

1. In what year did Steve Davis win his first world title in snooker?

2. Anthony Nesty of Surinam was in 1988 the first Olympic gold medallist from his country. What other distinction did he have at this Olympics?

3. Who knocked out Mike Tyson to take the world heavyweight crown in 1990, causing a major upset in boxing history?

4. Red Rum won the Grand National three times. Who was his trainer?

5. At the Berlin Olympics in 1936, black athlete Jesse Owens won the 100 metres, 200 metres and long jump. Who stormed out of the stadium in disgust?

6. What forced Nigel Mansell out of the 1986 Australian Grand Prix, robbing him of the world title?

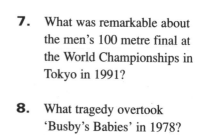

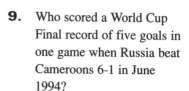

7. What was remarkable about the men's 100 metre final at the World Championships in Tokyo in 1991?

8. What tragedy overtook 'Busby's Babies' in 1978?

9. Who scored a World Cup Final record of five goals in one game when Russia beat Cameroons 6-1 in June 1994?

10. After the 1904 Olympic marathon the winner, Fred Lorz, was banned for life by the US Amateur Athletic Union. Why?

11. When was the first England v Australia Test match played?

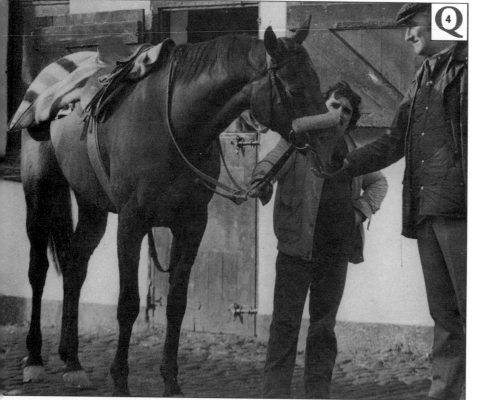

12. Who was the first gymnast in Olympic history to be awarded a perfect score, in the 1976 Games?

13. In the 1986 World Cup, Maradonna scored with what appeared to be a handball. What did he call this?

14. Who was the first footballer to be knighted?

15. In which year was the Olympic flame introduced to the modern games?

16. Who regained the World Heavyweight Boxing Championship twice?

17. Which motor racing star won the World Drivers' Championship five times in the 1950s?

18. Which pop-star raced a yacht named *Drum*?

19. In which event did Britain's Linford Christie win an Olympic gold in Barcelona?

20. In 1983, who scored a touchdown after the longest run from scrimmage in American football?

21. Who won the 5,000 metres, the 10,000 metres and also the Marathon in the 1952 Olympics?

22. Which Russian gymnast won many hearts in the 1972 Olympics with her charismatic performance on balance beam and floor exercise?

23. In 1988 the tallest gold medallist yet recorded competed in the Olympic Games in what sport?

24. In which sport did Gert Fredriksson win six Olympic gold medals?

25. Vitaly Scherbo won six golds at the 1992 Olympics representing the Commonwealth of Independent States in which sport?

Q 16

1. In which American state is the Grand Canyon?

2. What would you do with grissini?

3. Noah's ark came to rest on which mountain?

4. By what name is dyspepia usually known?

5. Which is the world's warmest sea?

6. To which group of painters do Monet, Sisley and Pisarro belong?

7. In which Orwell novel were some of the character 'more equal than others'?

8. According to the saying, who makes the best gamekeeper?

9. What does an anti-coagulant drug do?

10. Who killed Martin Luther King in 1968?

11. Name the dramatist who wrote *Entertaining Mr Sloane* and *Loot*?

12. What type of wine is Asti Spumante?

13. In which sport would you hear of roundhouse, knuckler and outcurve?

14. What do the letters MGM stand for?

15. The songs 'You'll Never Walk Alone' and 'If I Loved You' come from which musical?

16. Who designed Madonna's famous pointed corset?

17. Bibliomania is a compulsive desire for what?

18. Which film first teamed Ginger Rogers and Fred Astaire?

19. Dachshunds were bred as hunting dogs in Germany. What did they hunt?

20. In Australia, you might have the opportunity of seeing a corroboree. What is it?

21. Two of the types of particle present in an atom are proton and neutron. What is the third?

22. Cochise and Geronimo were chiefs of which Native American tribe?

23. What name was given to the Hindu custom whereby a widow would throw herself on the funeral pyre?

24. Inflammable means easily set on fire. What does flammable mean?

25. If you were reading Nagel and Baedeker what would you be planning?

Geography and Travel • Air, Land and Sea

1. Between Stockholm in Sweden and Helsinki in Finland
2. A tender
3. New York
4. Metro
5. The ship is fully loaded
6. 1877
7. Air resistance
8. Italy
9. Boeing 747
10. The first transatlantic crossing by hot-air balloon
11. USA
12. The first pedal-bicycle
13. Four days
14. Tourist Trophy
15. Union Pacific
16. Greenwich, London
17. To push passengers into crowded trains
18. Agatha Christie's
19. George Stephenson
20. From its pioneer, Dr Rudolf Diesel
21. Hydrofoil
22. Nautilus
23. Switzerland
24. About 3000BC
25. Robert Morley

Popular Culture • Signs of the Zodiac

1. A centaur drawing a bow
2. Sapphire
3. Aries, Leo and Sagittarius
4. The rat
5. Gemini
6. St Mark's Square
7. Air
8. Aquarius
9. Sagittarius
10. Ophiuchus
11. Libra
12. Taurus
13. The graphic symbols used to represent the signs
14. Aries
15. Cancer
16. Earth
17. The crayfish
18. 12
19. They swim in parallel
20. Capricorn
21. Pisces
22. Canterbury
23. The first and last days of the sign period
24. Gemini
25. 18

Indoors and Out • Health and Beauty

1. Saturated fat
2. Eight
3. 10
4. Pancreas
5. Aromatherapy
6. Naturally slender people
7. Endomorphs
8. Ear
9. A dye that produces a yellow colour
10. Natural Protection Time
11. Scarsdale diet
12. Thyroid
13. Remove the dead skin cells
14. Athlete's foot
15. Too low carbohydrate
16. After foundation and powder
17. 37°C (98.5°F)
18. Fruit
19. Diseases of the blood
20. It can cause defects in the unborn child
21. Reflexology
22. Oily at the scalp and dry at the ends
23. Kidneys
24. Posture
25. Eyes

Past and Present • Religious Affairs

1. Brigham Young
2. Christian
3. Ayatollah Khomeini
4. Sikh
5. India
6. From the protest of Luther and other church reformers
7. Brahma
8. Dalai Lama
9. Cape Town
10. Sunni and Shi'ite
11. Baha'i
12. Greek
13. 1970s
14. Philippines
15. Society of Friends or Quakers
16. Rastafarian
17. Nirvana
18. Pentecostal
19. Yin and yang; passive and active
20. St Augustine
21. Medina
22. Torah
23. In prison
24. Methodist
25. Reconstructionism

Youth World • Bears

1. 1903
2. 1950s
3. Polar bear
4. It gets all the moisture it needs from its diet of eucalyptus leaves
5. In the fork of a tree
6. A. A. Milne
7. Aloysius
8. Spectacled bear
9. They eat fruit and honey as well as meat and fish
10. Fozzie
11. Mishka
12. Termites
13. Davy Crockett
14. Goldilocks
15. Three years
16. American football
17. Joel Chandler Harris
18. John Betjeman
19. Alistair McLean
20. Sleeping high in a nest of twigs and branches
21. Brown bear
22. Mary Plain
23. Arctophily
24. January
25. Darkest Peru

Famous Folk • TV Stars

1. *Gladiators*
2. Actor, director, writer
3. Oprah Winfrey
4. Paul Eddington as Jim Hacker
5. Jane Seymour
6. Mitch Buchannon
7. Martin Sheen
8. Inspector Morse
9. Debbie Allen
10. Chat shows
11. Arnie Becker
12. Michael Douglas
13. *A Touch of Frost*
14. William Hartnell
15. David Attenborough
16. Victor Meldrew
17. Cherie Lunghi
18. Jimmy Smits
19. Anthony Edwards
20. Grace Bros
21. Robert Culp
22. *Rawhide*
23. Robert Vaughn
24. Jack Rosenthal
25. Patrick Swayze

Sport and Leisure • Sporting Moments

1. 1981
2. He was the first black swimmer to win an Olympic event
3. James 'Buster' Douglas
4. Donald 'Ginger' McCain
5. Adolf Hitler
6. An exploding tyre
7. It produced four of the fastest times ever recorded in the event
8. The Munich air crash
9. Oleg Salenko
10. He was taken part of the way by car
11. 1877
12. Nadia Comaneci
13. 'The hand of God'
14. Stanley Matthews
15. 1928
16. Muhammad Ali
17. Juan Fangio
18. Simon Le Bon
19. Men's 100 metres
20. Tony Dorsett
21. Emil Zatopek
22. Olga Korbut
23. Basketball
24. Canoe racing
25. Gymnastics

Pot Luck

1. Arizona
2. Eat them
3. Ararat
4. Indigestion
5. Red Sea
6. Impressionist
7. *Animal Farm*
8. An old poacher
9. It stops blood clotting
10. James Earl Ray
11. Joe Orton
12. Sparkling
13. Baseball
14. Metro-Goldwyn-Mayer
15. *Carousel*
16. Jean Paul Gaultier
17. Books
18. *Flying Down To Rio*
19. Badgers
20. An Aboriginal dance ceremony
21. Electron
22. Apache
23. Suttee
24. The same: easily set on fire
25. Travel

1. Which Russian fortress, incorporating palaces and churches, became the seat of modern government?

2. Where would you find the Palace of Nurturing the Heart, the Palace of Heavenly Purity and the Palace of Peaceful Longevity?

3. The Palace of Versailles was built by which French king?

4. Which 15th-century palace in Florence houses the Palatine Gallery, with its collections of paintings made by the Medici princes in the 17th and 18th centuries?

5. Name the romantic poet who lived in Dove Cottage and Rydal Mount in the English Lake District.

6. On which famous river would you find the Cat and Mouse Castles?

7. Many plantation homes survive in the deep south of the US. What was the name of the O'Hara family home in *Gone with the Wind*?

8. The palace of Schönbrunn, built between 1696 and 1713, was the summer home of which royal house?

9. What English name is usually given to the Palazzo Ducale in Venice?

10. The Treaty House on the shore of the Bay of Islands is important in the history of New Zealand. Whose representatives signed the Treaty of Waitangi in 1840?

11. Whitehall, once the opulent home of Henry Morrison Flagler, is in Palm Beach, Florida. In what business did Flagler make his millions?

12. Neuschwanstein, the fairytale castle built by King Ludwig II, is one of Germany's top tourist attractions. In which part of Germany is it located?

13. Which castle, belonging to the English Crown for over 900 years, is open to the public again, following a disastrous fire?

14. The Winter Palace in St Petersburg, now Russia's Hermitage Museum, was built in the mid-18th century in what architectural style?

15. A 1964 film starring Peter Ustinov and Melina Mercouri told the story of jewel thieves planning a robbery at Istanbul's 15th-century palace. What is its name?

16. In which eastern European city would you find the Palais Palffy, Palais Kolovrat and Palais Furstenburg, all with elegant 18th-century facades?

17. Vita Sackville-West and Sir Harold Nicholson made a famous garden in the grounds of Sissinghurst Castle. In which English county is Sissinghurst?

18. Switzerland's Chateau de Chillon, the 13th-century castle with grim dungeons, inspired which poet to write *The Prison of Chillon*?

19. The Palazzo Vecchio, once the ducal palace and new city hall, is the symbol of Florence. What is its other name?

20. Cairo's sumptuous Manial Palace, built in 1901 by a royal prince, is in which part of the city?

21. Anna Leonowens, an English governess whose story inspired a musical show and two films, was a governess to royal children in the Grand Palace in which city?

22. Spain's Alhambra has a grove of great elms, called the Alameda, in the grounds. Which British statesman had them planted during the Peninsular War?

Q 14

23. Colonial Williamsburg is America's unique restoration project, re-creating an 18th-century town. In which state is Williamsburg?

24. Holyrood House, in Edinburgh, is the official Scottish residence of Queen Elizabeth II. What does the name mean?

25. In which country is the Sacred Valley of the Incas, with its terraced fortress of Ollantytambo?

1. Which band was named after a character in the film *Barbarella*?

2. How did Buddy Holly die?

3. Matt Sorum joined Guns 'n' Roses from which group?

4. Which Michael Jackson album sold 41 million copies?

5. George Michael went on to a number of solo hits after splitting from Andrew Ridgeley in 1986. What was the duo called?

6. Who won Grammy awards for 'Saving All My Love For You' and 'I Wanna Dance with Somebody' and was chosen to sing America's Olympic anthem 'One Moment in Time' in 1988?

7. Soca is Caribbean music. How does it get its name?

8. *Dark Side of the Moon* sold 10 million copies worldwide. Which group recorded the album?

9. Which rock band, among the earliest fronted by a woman, recorded the albums *Brigade*, *Bad Animals* and *Dreamboat Annie*?

10. Whose only hit was 'Shaddup Your Face'?

11. Which group had a hit with 'Love is All Around' in 1994?

12. Name the pop star who played the leader of a teenage gang in the film *Quadrophenia*?

13. What was the debut single for Take That, securing them a major record contract with RCA?

14. 'Touch Me in the Morning' was a hit for which singer?

15. Who is nicknamed 'His Royal Badness'?

16. Which rock star, one of the highest paid performers of the 1980s, married top model Christie Brinkley?

17. Whose first album was *Are You Experienced*?

18. What type of music is salsa, made popular by Puerto Ricans in New York in the 1980s?

19. Who won the 1990 BRITS award for Top British Group and returned it, saying that the awards show was used to promote Margaret Thatcher?

20. The Pet Shop Boys were formed in 1981. Name them.

21. What was the former name of the group Led Zeppelin?

22. Which teen pop group had seven top 10 singles in the UK in 1990, the first time an American group had achieved this?

23. Who created the 'wall of sound' in the mid-1960s?

24. How many albums does an artist have to sell to go platinum?

25. What type of music would headbangers listen to?

Q 8

5. Which country is the largest wine producer in South America?

6. From 1920 to 1933 alcohol was banned in America. What was this era called?

7. Where does Marsala come from?

8. What colour wine is produced by Merlot and Syrah grapes?

9. Is better wine produced if it is aged in new oak barrels or old?

10. Which is the lightest style of sherry?

11. Which is the fullest and richest style of sherry?

12. Besides gin, what are the ingredients of a White Lady cocktail?

13. An old enemy of the vine is phylloxera. What is it?

14. A new enemy of the vine is eutypia dieback. What is it?

15. What name is given to the German wine made from grapes that have been left on the vine over winter?

16. Where are the Sonoma and Napa Valley wine-growing areas?

17. If a wine was described as aggressive, what would it be?

1. Which country has the largest area under vine?

2. On a German wine label, what would 'trocken' mean?

3. In one method of red winemaking, the grapes are fermented in bunches under a layer of carbon dioxide instead of being crushed. What is this method called?

4. If grapes are harvested slightly late, what happens to their flavour?

18. Where does the name whisky come from?

19. The south of France, because of its willingness to experiment, is known as what?

20. Hungary has the oldest wine tradition in Eastern Europe. Which is its most famous wine?

21. What did the Rev. Elijah Craig start distilling in Georgetown, Virginia in 1789?

22. In Germany, what is supposed to be the equivalent of the French 'vin de pays'?

23. What is the equivalent of the French 'vin de pays' in Spanish wine?

24. In which decade did the white wine boom begin for Australian producers?

25. The cocktail Yankee Invigorator contains brandy, port, sugar, egg and what else?

Q 9

Q 16

4. What was unusual about the crowning of Hatshepsut, who reigned Egypt for 20 years?

5. Who was the Egyptian god of the dead?

6. The main measurement in Egypt was the cubit. How long was a cubit?

7. Which king built the great temple of Karnak, still to be seen near Luxor in Egypt?

8. Which of the seven wonders of the ancient world was at Ephesus?

9. What ancient civilization flourished in Crete?

10. In 1500 BC there was a volcanic eruption on an island near Crete. Some historians believe that it did so much damage that the great civilization never recovered. Name the island.

11. Into how many tribes were the Israelites divided?

12. Which race dominated the Israelites in Palestine for nearly 200 years?

13. After the death of King Solomon the Israelite kingdom was split in two. Israel had its capital at Shechem. Where was Judah's capital?

14. What is an ankh?

15. Which Greek poet told the story of the Trojan war?

1. Between which two rivers was the land of Mesopotamia?

2. Among which people do we find the first evidence of the use of wheels?

3. Where did the Vikings believe their warriors were taken after death?

16. The sight of a Viking ship would have struck fear into the hearts of the Scots or English in early days. How were these ships propelled?

17. Where did the Greeks believe the souls of the wicked would go to suffer eternal punishment?

18. Which empire was conquered by Alexander the Great between 334 BC and 331 BC?

19. Who was the most important god of the Vikings?

20. Which of the seven wonders of the ancient world stood at Rhodes?

21. The ancient Olypmpic Games were started in 776 BC. How often did they take place?

22. Why did the ancient Olympic Games end in 395 BC?

23. Civil war in the Roman Republic culminated in 63 BC in the First Triumvirate under Caesar, Crassus and which third leader?

24. Egyptian gods were often identified with animals – for instance, Anubis with the jackal and Sekmet with the lioness. With which animal was Horus identified?

25. In the centre of a Roman town there was an open area, surrounded by the buildings of government. What was it called?

Q18

5. In the Roald Dahl book, who runs a chocolate factory?

6. Which boys' hero has friends called Algy Lacy and Ginger Hebblethwaite?

7. What is the real name of super heroine Wonder Woman?

8. Who wrote the children's novel *Chitty Chitty Bang Bang*?

9. In *Alice in Wonderland*, what did the Queen of Hearts yell at those who annoyed her?

10. Which little girl would get her own way by threatening to scream and scream until she was sick?

11. *National Velvet* was originally a novel by Enid Bagnold. Who played Velvet in the 1944 film?

1. Robin Williams plays Mrs Doubtfire in the film of that name. Who wrote the book on which it is based?

2. In which book does Bilbo Baggins first appear?

3. What nationality was Little Lord Fauntleroy?

4. Which character, with friends including Mole and Rat, has a passion for fast cars?

12. Which elephant first appeared in a book by Jean de Brunhoff, published in France in 1931?

13. In *The Jungle Book*, who is the boy raised in the Indian forests?

14. The lead strip of the British *Eagle* comic featured which heroic space pilot?

15. What word does Billy Batson need to say to transform himself into Captain Marvel?

16. Which doctor lives in Puddleby-on-the-Marsh and talks to animals?

17. Name the novel in which Mary Lennox becomes friends with Dickon and Colin.

18. Which comic strip heroine did Jane Fonda play in a 1964 film?

19. Who wrote about Noddy and Big-Ears?

20. In which American state did Tom Sawyer and Huckleberry Finn have their adventures?

21. Tintin, red-haired cub reporter, first appeared in comic strips in the 1920s and later in an animated TV series and two films. In which country was he invented?

22. A race of pixie-like creatures became popular throughout Europe from the 1960s onwards after they appeared in a Belgian comic-strip and were used to sell a wide variety of merchandise. In French they were 'Les Schtroumpfs'. Who are they in English?

23. In an American novel by Jean Webster, orphaned Judy Abbott writes a series of letters to an unknown benefactor and eventually meets and falls in love with him. What is her nickname for him?

24. Who is the young narrator of Robert Louis Stevenson's novel *Treasure Island*?

25. Who are Homily, Pod and little Arriety?

1. When T. E. Lawrence returned from Arabia, he tried to become anonymous. Give either of the false names he used.

2. The French motor racing champion of 1985, 1986 and 1989 was nicknamed 'The Professor'. Who was he?

3. What is Madonna's real first name?

4. Eric and Ernie took the names Morecambe and Wise because their own surnames were too long for the billboards. What were they?

5. Which boxer was known as Smokin' Joe?

6. The novels of Mary Ann Evans became famous in the 19th century and are classics today. What name did Mary Ann Evans write under?

7. What is pop star Sting's real name?

8. By what name is Peter Sutcliffe better known?

9. Big Daddy and Giant Haystacks are both wrestlers. Which one's real name is Shirley Crabtree?

10. Zsa Zsa Gabor changed only her first name. What was it originally?

11. Under what name is sportsman Edson Arantes do Nascimento better known?

14. Give the real name of rock star Adam Ant.

15. Nikolai Poliakov became which well-known circus performer?

16. What name does Stephen Judkins use?

17. Which prolific Victorian novelist was known as 'Boz'?

18. US singer, songwriter and record producer William Robinson exchanged his first name for what nickname?

19. Born in 1914 as Joseph Barrow, he became known as the 'Brown Bomber'. Who was he?

20. Doris Kappelhoff changed only her last name. What did she choose?

21. Which boxer was known as the Manassa Mauler?

22. In 1925 MGM ran a contest to find a new name for Lucille Le Sueur. What did they decide on?

23. John Wayne Gacy was one of America's most sadistic mass murderers. What was he often called?

24. Which US baseball player was known as the Georgia Peach?

25. During World War II, how was William Joyce better known?

12. Singer Arnold Dorsey changed his name and never looked back. What name does he use now?

13. What are the first names of novelist P. D. James?

1. When petrol-powered vehicles first replaced those drawn by horses, what were they called?

2. The body of a car is now built in one unit. The body used to be mounted on a wood or metal structure. What was it called?

3. Which famous film star is the joint owner of an Indy car racing team?

4. Where is the Italian Grand Prix held?

5. Cars usually race with 'slicks'. What are they?

6. In drag racing a series of lamps flash a countdown sequence to the start. What are the lamps called?

7. What colour were all Model T Fords?

8. What type of car is the Impact, produced by General Motors?

9. Ayrton Senna had his first Brazilian Grand Prix win in 1985. What nationality was he?

10. Which country do you associate with the production of Renault cars?

11. In the Belgian Grand Prix of 1994 which driver was disqualified, giving Damon Hill the victory?

12. Thorpe and Salter made the first car speedometer in 1910. What speeds did it cover?

13. At a race meeting, what does a white flag mean?

14. At a race meeting, what warning does a red and yellow striped flag give?

15. Which British father and son both held the land speed record?

16. Championship Auto Racing Teams (CART) make the rules for which type of racing?

17. Which driver's racing career ended with a serious accident in Indianapolis in 1992, when he suffered multiple leg injuries?

18. The first Grand Prix World Championship was held in 1950. Who won?

19. What does a differential gear enable the wheels of a car to do?

20. Formula One cars must weigh a minimum of 500 kg. What is the minimum for Indy cars?

21. Name the father of Formula One star Damon Hill.

22. Which country do you associate with the manufacture of Nissan cars?

23. Who was the first posthumous world champion?

24. Who won the 1995 Formula One driver's title?

25. On a wet road, a tyre may lose its grip and ride on a film of water so that the driver loses control. What is this called?

Q 7

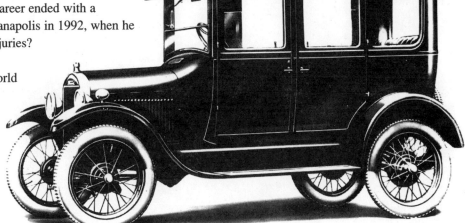

1. In the Bible, who is turned into a pillar of salt?

2. How many sides has a prism?

3. In Britain it is called a truncheon. What is it called in America?

4. With which song did Abba win the European Song Contest?

5. Pastrami is a highly seasoned type of what?

6. In which English county are Winston Graham's Poldark novels set?

7. What is another name for the linden tree?

8. Who was shot as he left the Washington Hilton in 1981?

9. Which TV series had a character called Potsie?

10. What do the author Thackeray's initials, W. M., stand for?

11. In which country did Father's Day first become a day for cards and presents?

12. Which painter portrayed the life of 19th-century Paris bars and music halls?

13. Imran Khan is a famous cricketer. Which country does he come from?

14. Who went to sea in a beautiful pea-green boat?

15. What blood relation was Prince Albert to Queen Victoria?

16. If a Native American tribe used 'wampum' as currency, what would they be paying with?

17. The following are three American Presidents assassinated while in office: Lincoln, McKinley and Kennedy. Name the fourth.

18. What did the 'lolly ladies' do in English theatres?

19. Soyuz is a name given to Russian spacecraft. What does it mean?

20. The largest lake in Africa is Lake Victoria. Which countries is it bounded by?

21. In the song, how long is Campdown race track?

22. Give the common name for the trachea.

23. What is the highest British decoration for bravery?

24. In the 18th century, what sort of young man would be called a 'macaroni'?

25. The film *Midnight Express* was about a young American's experiences in prison in which country?

Geography and Travel • Houses and Palaces

1. The Kremlin
2. The Forbidden City, Beijing
3. Louis XIV
4. Pitti Palace
5. William Wordsworth
6. Rhine
7. Tara
8. Hapsburgs
9. Doge's Palace
10. Representatives of the Maoris and the British government
11. Railroads
12. Bavarian Alps
13. Windsor Castle
14. Baroque
15. *Topkapi*
16. Prague
17. Kent
18. Lord Byron
19. Palazzo della Signoria
20. Roda Island
21. Bangkok
22. Duke of Wellington
23. Virginia
24. Holy Cross
25. Peru

Popular Culture • Rock and Pop

1. Duran Duran
2. Air crash
3. The Cult
4. *Thriller*
5. Wham!
6. Whitney Houston
7. It is a mixture of soul and calypso
8. Pink Floyd
9. Heart
10. Joe Dolce
11. Wet Wet Wet
12. Sting
13. 'Do What You Like'
14. Diana Ross
15. Prince
16. Billy Joel
17. Jimi Hendrix
18. Latin big band dance music
19. Five Young Cannibals
20. Neil Tennant and Chris Lowe
21. The Yarbirds
22. New Kids on the Block
23. Phil Spector
24. One million
25. Heavy metal

Indoors and Out • Wines and Spirits

1. Spain
2. Dry
3. Carbonic maceration
4. The acidity will drop
5. Argentina
6. Prohibition
7. Sicily
8. Red
9. New
10. Manzanilla
11. Olorosa
12. Lemon juice and Cointreau
13. An aphid
14. A fungus
15. Eiswein
16. California
17. Young, or unmellowed older wine
18. The Gaelic, uisge beatha
19. The new California
20. Tokay
21. Bourbon
22. Landwein
23. Vino de la tierra
24. 1970s
25. Coffee

Past and Present • Early Civilizations

1. Tigris and Euphrates
2. Sumerians
3. Valhalla
4. She was crowned king, not queen; rulers had to be considered male
5. Osiris
6. The distance from elbow to fingertip
7. Rameses II
8. Temple of Artemis
9. Minoan
10. Thíra or Santorini
11. Twelve
12. Philistines
13. Jerusalem
14. An Egyptian amulet worn as a charm
15. Homer
16. By both oars and sails
17. Tartarus
18. Persian
19. Odin
20. Colossus
21. Every four years
22. Olympia was destroyed by earthquake
23. Pompey
24. Falcon
25. Forum

Youth World • Books and Comics

1. Anne Fine
2. *The Hobbit*
3. American
4. Toad
5. Willie Wonka
6. Biggles
7. Diana Prince
8. Ian Fleming
9. 'Off with his head!'
10. Violet Elizabeth Bott
11. Elizabeth Taylor
12. Barbar
13. Mowgli
14. Dan Dare
15. Shazam
16. Dr Dolittle
17. *The Secret Garden*
18. Barbarella
19. Enid Blyton
20. Mississippi
21. Belgium
22. Smurfs
23. Daddy Long-Legs
24. Jim Hawkins
25. The Borrowers

Famous Folk • True Identity

1. Ross and Shaw
2. Alain Prost
3. Madonna
4. Bartholomew and Wiseman
5. Joe Frazier
6. George Eliot
7. Gordon Sumner
8. The Yorkshire Ripper
9. Big Daddy
10. Sari
11. Pelé
12. Engelbert Humperdinck
13. Phyllis Dorothy
14. Stuart Goddard
15. Coco the Clown
16. Stevie Wonder
17. Charles Dickens
18. Smokey
19. Joe Louis
20. Day
21. Jack Dempsey
22. Joan Crawford
23. The Killer Clown
24. Ty Cobb
25. Lord Haw-Haw

Sport and Leisure • Cars and Driving

1. Horseless carriages
2. Chassis
3. Paul Newman
4. Monza
5. Smooth tyres with no tread
6. Christmas tree
7. Black
8. It runs on electricity
9. Brazilian
10. France
11. Michael Schumacher
12. 0–35 mph
13. Ambulance or rescue vehicles on the track
14. Slippery surface
15. Michael and Donald Campbell
16. Indy car
17. Nelson Picquet
18. Guiseppe Farina
19. Rotate at different speeds round corners
20. 703 kg
21. Graham Hill
22. Japan
23. Jochen Rindt
24. Michael Schumacher
25. Aquaplaning

Pot Luck

1. Lot's wife
2. Five
3. Night-stick
4. 'Waterloo'
5. Beef
6. Cornwall
7. Lime
8. President Reagan
9. *Happy Days*
10. William Makepeace
11. USA
12. Toulouse-Lautrec
13. Pakistan
14. The owl and the pussycat
15. First cousin
16. Beads made of shells
17. Garfield
18. They sold oranges
19. Union
20. Kenya, Uganda, Tanzania
21. Five miles
22. Windpipe
23. Victoria Cross
24. He would be a dandy, wearing fashionable clothes from the continent
25. Turkey

1. If a volcano is neither active nor extinct, what is it?

2. Rock made of coarse sand is called sandstone. What is rock made from layers of thin mud and clay called?

3. Where would you find a delta?

4. What type of mountains are the Himalayas?

5. The Richter scale measures the magnitude of an earthquake. What does the Mercalli scale measure?

6. What is another name for a limestone landscape?

7. The bulk of the island of Tenerife is one volcanic mountain. Name the mountain.

8. On the ground of the rainforest, there is a layer of rotting leaves and vegetation. What is it called?

9. Which is the world's largest volcanic crater?

10. How much of an iceberg is submerged?

11. What name is given to rocks formed from other rocks changed in some way, usually by heat or pressure?

12. Which is the longest mountain range in North America?

13. What are the world's three main fossil fuels?

14. In the tundra regions, the soil and often the bedrock is permanently frozen. What is this called?

15. What type of valleys are those formed by land subsiding between two parallel faults?

16. The chain of volcanic activity around the Pacific Ocean is called what?

17. What name is given to the continuous action of waves on the shore whereby sand and shingle are moved along the beach?

18. In 1883 Krakatoa was the greatest volcanic explosion in modern times. Where was Krakatoa?

19. What is the tallest type of grass?

20. The Vinson Massif is the highest mountain in which continent?

21. The removal of salt from water which is then used for irrigation or drinking is known as what?

22. What is a honeypot area?

23. What is the name for rocks which water cannot pass through?

24. What name is given to the point on the earth's surface directly above the focus of an earthquake?

25. Which part of the earth's structure, rich in silica, lies between the core and the crust?

1. Which Australian sometimes appears as the 'cultural attaché to the Court of St James'?

2. What is Sergeant Bilko's first name?

3. Which film stars Anthony Hopkins and is billed as 'a comedy of the heart and other organs'?

4. What was the profession of Cliff Huxtable, Bill Cosby's character in *The Cosby Show*?

5. Which member of the comedy duo Laurel and Hardy was born in England?

6. Who plays the dim member of *The Golden Girls*?

7. What was the name of the piano-playing dog in *The Muppet Show*?

8. Which successful fat comic starred in *The Great Outdoors* and *Uncle Buck*?

9. What did Mork in *Mork and Mindy* mean when he said 'Nanoo, nanoo' in his own language?

10. Name the film in which Arnold Schwarzenegger becomes pregnant.

11. Which American actress and comedienne created Ernestine the telephone operator and Trudy the bag-lady?

12. Who was George Burns' wife and comedy partner?

13. Denis Norden hosts *It'll be Alright on the Night* on British TV, showing clips of all sorts of mistakes made during filming. What do Americans call these shows?

14. Which was the first of the *Carry On* films?

15. In *Roseanne*, who plays the star's husband?

16. Who took over from Johnny Carson in *The Tonight Show* on American television?

17. Name the play by Victoria Wood in which two sisters are unwillingly reunited by a TV show.

18. In which TV sit-com did Mollie Sugden play Mrs Slocombe?

19. In which film do Jack Lemmon and Tony Curtis dress in drag?

20. Which British TV comic had his contract cancelled in 1988 and went on to become a big star on American TV?

21. Who stars as a self-confessed serial-monogamist in *Four Weddings and a Funeral*?

22. Which character is played by Ted Danson in *Cheers*?

23. Name the gentle, accident-prone French eccentric portrayed by Jacques Tati.

24. Lucille Ball and Desi Arnaz starred in *I Love Lucy*, which was made by their own production company. What was the company called?

25. Which British comedy magician collapsed on stage and died during a televised theatre show, *Live at Her Majesty's*?

1. What is the largest carnivore in the African savannah?

2. What gives the bald eagle its name?

3. How does the boa constrictor kill its prey?

4. The survival of some Arctic species of predator depends on the availability of which animals?

5. What habit gives the praying mantis its name?

6. Which predator was accused of taking and killing the Chamberlain baby in Australia?

7. The cheetah is the fastest land animal. Roughly what speed can it reach?

8. How do puff adders disable their prey?

9. The peregrine, highly prized by falconers, is found on every continent but one. Which is it?

10. At what age are tigers fully grown?

11. Which predator often follows the polar bear, feeding on the abandoned carcass of its kill?

12. What type of animal is a meerkat?

13. Which is larger, the grey or red wolf?

14. What family of animals does the serval belong to?

15. In the polar lands, which type of seal is the main enemy of penguins?

16. What is the other name for the beluga whale?

17. Which type of predators can be pygmy, scops and eagle?

18. Coyotes, found all over America, pair for life. True or false?

19. How does the crocodile prepare to lay its eggs?

20. Piranha fish have a fearsome reputation for their attacks on animals and humans, reducing them to skeletons in a matter of minutes. In what part of the world are they found?

21. What is a female walrus called?

22. Which is the largest and most aggressive of the three hyena species?

23. Spiders spin silk webs to catch insects. The silk is spun from organs at the end of the abdomen. What are they called?

24. What do leopards do with a kill, to protect the meat from other predators?

25. What is the name of the African cat whose anal glands secrete a strong smelling substance used in perfume manufacture?

1. Where did Edwin Drake drill the first production oil well in 1819?

2. What valuable resource was discovered in South Africa's Orange Free State in 1867?

3. In what year did the Great Exhibition open at Crystal Palace in London?

4. Who was known as the father of the factory system because of his invention of a spinning machine?

5. What did Jethro Tull invent in the early 1700s, making better harvesting possible?

6. In which decade of the 19th century was the refrigerator first successfully developed?

7. The world's first iron bridge was erected in which English county in 1779?

8. What name was given to the factory-hands whose objective was to destroy the new factory machinery?

9. Benjamin Franklin proved that lightning is a form of electricity by flying a kite in a thunderstorm. What did he go on to invent?

10. Which poet wrote about the 'dark satanic mills' of the Industrial Revolution?

11. The Suez Canal was opened in 1869. Which seas did it link?

12. What kind of British settlers started arriving in Australia by the shipload in 1788?

13. The musical show *Les Miserables* was based on a novel about the plight of the poor, written in 1862. Who was the author?

14. Which American mail order firm was established in 1886, growing very quickly over the next decade?

15. The Caribbean and the Pacific Ocean were linked by which canal in 1914?

16. Who was the world's first oil billionaire?

17. Who wrote the *Communist Manifesto* in 1848, stating that workers were wage slaves?

18. Which reformer's Abolition Bill ended the British slave trade in 1801?

19. The first successful revolver was patented by which American gunsmith in 1835?

20. Which railway was completed in 1886, linking the Pacific and the Atlantic?

21. For what event was the Eiffel Tower erected in 1889?

22. Brunel was responsible for building three of the greatest 19th-century ships and was the chief engineer of the Great Western Railway. What was his full name?

23. Charles Dickens exposed many of the evils of Victorian England in his books. In which novel did he write about half-starved workhouse children?

24. Canals came later to America than Europe. In 1825, which canal linked the Great Lakes to the Atlantic Ocean?

25. A machine gun capable of firing 600 rounds a minute was invented in 1862 and named after its inventor. Who was he?

1. Which was Disney's first full-length feature?

2. In *Fantasia*, who was the sorcerer's apprentice?

3. In *Fantasia*, what task does the sorcerer's apprentice try to dodge by using magic?

4. Who played Captain Nemo in the 1954 film *20,000 Leagues Under the Sea*?

5. *One Hundred and One Dalmatians* was based on a novel by which author?

6. Name the villainess in *One Hundred and One Dalmatians*.

7. What unique ability does Dumbo have?

8. Which nanny could slide up banisters and fly with the help of an umbrella?

9. Disney's film *Pinocchio* was released in 1939. It was based on a children's classic from which country?

10. Who is Pinocchio's conscience?

11. In *Bambi*, what was the unlikely name given to the skunk?

12. *Swiss Family Robinson* was adapted from Johann Wyss's novel. Who was the star?

13. What was the name of the Volkswagen car that featured in several slapstick comedies?

14. What is the name of the Lion King?

15. Which film tells the story of a pedigree cat called Duchess who falls on hard times and meets up with an alley-cat called O'Malley?

16. In *Bedknobs and Broomsticks*, who played the amateur witch Eglantine Price?

17. What type of dog is Nana in *Peter Pan*?

18. *The Sword in the Stone* tells the story of whose boyhood?

19. In which film do the aristocratic Siamese Si and Am make their appearance?

20. Hayley Mills played Pollyanna in the 1960 film. What was Pollyanna's way of tackling setbacks and disappointments?

21. In *Robin Hood*, the title character was portrayed as which animal?

22. Which comic actor starred in several films, including *The Absent-Minded Professor* and *The Shaggy Dog*?

23. Who is the teller of tales in *Song of the South*?

24. What did absent-minded scientist Moranis do in his 1989 adventure?

25. *In Search of the Castaways* was an adaptation of which author's novel?

1. 'Seasons of mists and mellow fruitfulness, Close bosom-friend of the maturing sun'. Who wrote this description of autumn?

2. In which novel does Ernest Hemingway write about a Cuban fisherman fighting nature in pursuit of a marlin?

3. Patrick White was born in London but in which country did he live and set novels like *The Happy Valley* and *The Tree of Man*?

4. Who was the angry young man of the 1950s who wrote *Look Back in Anger*?

5. Which poet wrote about a sailor who was punished for killing an albatross?

6. *Lady Chatterley's Lover* was the subject of an obscenity trial in Britain in 1959. Who was the author?

7. Rudyard Kipling wrote a famous novel about his childhood in India. What was it called?

8. Name the New Zealand writer, famed for her short stories, who married critic and editor John Middleton Murry and suffered from tuberculosis?

9. Which poet wrote the story of the Lady of Shalott?

10. What narrative technique do James Joyce and William Faulkner use in their novels?

11. Who wrote about the feuding inhabitants of Wuthering Heights?

12. The musical *Cats* was based on the poems of T. S. Eliot. Whose *Book of Practical Cats* did he write?

13. In which play did Shakespeare write about Claudius, Ophelia and Polonius?

14. Alexander Solzhenitsyn suffered prison and exile in the USSR for his anti-Stalinist views between 1945 and 1957. In which famous book did he expose the reality of the Soviet labour camps?

15. Name the American 19th-century poetess who was a recluse by the age of 30, dressing in white and carrying on friendships through correspondence.

16. Henry Fonda starred in the film based on John Steinbeck's novel about farm workers who were refugees from the dust bowl region. Name it.

17. What type of books does modern novelist Ramsey Campbell write?

18. Which poet wrote to a skylark: 'Hail to thee, blithe Spirit'?

19. Name the Norwegian dramatist who wrote *The Wild Duck* and *Hedda Gabler*.

20. What were Lord Byron's first names?

21. US writer James Baldwin wrote about what contemporary issue?

22. Charles Dickens wrote about Charles Darney, Madame Defarge and Dr Manette in which novel?

23. Which 19th-century playwright spent two years in Reading prison and wrote a ballad about his experiences?

24. Name the author of *Tender is the Night* and *The Last Tycoon*.

25. Shakespeare wrote the following opening lines for which play: 'If music be the food of love, play on'?

GOLF

1. What is the name given to one stroke over par for a hole?

2. The early type of ball was a leather case full of feathers. True or false?

3. The four biggest championships in golf are the Masters, the British Open, the US Open and which other?

4. What name is given to all four championships together?

5. In what way does the Masters differ from the other major championships?

6. Tom·Morris was the youngest golfer ever to win the British Open. How old was he?

7. What is another name for a bunker?

8. A shot that starts straight and curves slightly to the right is called what?

9. In which year did America lose the Ryder Cup for the first time ever?

10. What is shouted to warn players ahead of an approaching ball?

11. Which are the medium irons?

12. What is an albatross?

13. What do Americans call an albatross?

14. Who holds the record for the most wins in a US season?

15. St Andrews is the oldest golf course in Britain. True or false?

16. What is called the 'game within a game'?

17. Who is the biggest-ever money winner among women golfers?

18. What is another name for the flagstick?

19. Which are the short irons?

20. In 1994 Nick Price won the US PGA Championship. Which country does he come from?

21. Arnold Palmer is known for his 'come from behind' victories. What are they called?

22. What is a birdie?

23. Who is the world's best-paid golfer?

24. What does a 'shag bag' hold?

25. A player who regularly plays below his current handicap is called what?

Q5

5. What was Steve McQueen's last film?

6. In an orchestra, what is a tam-tam?

7. Which famous composer wrote the music which 'Twinkle, twinkle little star' is sung to?

8. Name the English painter who was exposed as a prolific art forger, having produced more than 2,000 fakes. He died in 1984.

9. Which author created Tarzan?

10. What breed of dog is Scooby Doo?

11. In the Black Forest area in Germany, religious families lay an extra place at the Christmas table. Who is it for?

12. Which city is the capital of Iceland?

13. Name the US playwright who wrote *Barefoot in the Park* and *The Odd Couple*.

14. In which disaster film is an ocean liner overturned by a massive wave?

15. The British call them estate agents. What do Americans call them?

16. What was the name of Evelyn Waugh's elder brother, who was also a well-known novelist?

17. The Pope wears a signet ring which portrays St Peter in a boat. What is this ring often called?

1. In which English county is Blenheim Palace?

2. What are Nahum, Haggai and Malachi?

3. The Kiel canal links the Baltic Sea with which other sea?

4. Which TV series was based on *The Raj Quartet* by Paul Scott?

18. What type of creature is an ale-wife?

19. If a horse is golden in colour with cream or white mane and tail, what is it called?

20. What name is given to the 'halo' of gas that surrounds the sun?

21. In music, what is a pastiche?

22. What name is given to a piece of rock from space that reaches the surface of the earth?

23. Which airport serves the city of Venice?

24. 'Apples and pears' is Cockney rhyming slang for what?

25. The Beatles were awarded which honour in 1965?

Geography and Travel • Features of the Land

1. Dormant
2. Shale
3. Where a river enters the sea
4. Fold mountains
5. The intensity of an earthquake
6. Karst
7. Mount Teide
8. Leaf litter
9. Mount Aso, Japan
10. About 80%
11. Metamorphic rocks
12. Rockies
13. Coal, oil and natural gas
14. Permafrost
15. Rift
16. Ring of fire
17. Longshore drift
18. Between Java and Sumatra
19. Bamboo
20. Antarctica
21. Desalination
22. A tourist area, more luxurious and therefore more popular than the surrounding area or country
23. Impermeable
24. Epicentre
25. Mantle

Popular Culture • Comedy

1. Barry Humphries
2. Ernest
3. *The Road to Wellville*
4. Obstetrician
5. Stan Laurel
6. Betty White
7. Rowlf
8. John Candy
9. Hello
10. *Junior*
11. Lily Tomlin
12. Gracie Allen
13. Blooper shows
14. *Carry on Sergeant*
15. John Goodman
16. Jay Leno
17. *Pat and Margaret*
18. *Are You Being Served?*
19. *Some Like It Hot*
20. Benny Hill
21. Hugh Grant
22. Sam Malone
23. Monsieur Hulot
24. Desilu Productions
25. Tommy Cooper

Indoors and Out • Predators

1. Lion
2. White feathers on the head
3. By squeezing it, causing suffocation
4. Lemmings
5. When it is awaiting its prey, its fore legs are held out in front of its body
6. Dingo
7. 100 km/h (62 mph)
8. With a venomous bite
9. Antarctica
10. Three
11. Arctic fox
12. Mongoose
13. Grey
14. Cat family
15. Leopard seal
16. White whale
17. Owls
18. True
19. It digs a pit
20. South and Central America
21. Cow
22. Spotted or laughing hyena
23. Spinnerets
24. Carry it into a tree
25. Civet

Past and Present • Age of Industry

1. Titusville, Pennsylvania
2. Diamonds
3. 1851
4. Richard Arkwright
5. Seed drill
6. 1860s
7. Shropshire
8. Luddites
9. Lightning conductor
10. William Blake
11. Mediterranean Sea and Indian Ocean via the Red Sea
12. Convicts
13. Victor Hugo
14. Sears Roebuck
15. Panama Canal
16. John D. Rockefeller
17. Karl Marx and Friedrich Engels
18. William Wilberforce
19. Samuel Colt
20. Canadian Pacific
21. Paris International Exposition
22. Isambard Kingdom Brunel
23. *Oliver Twist*
24. Erie Canal
25. Richard Gatling

Youth World • Disney Films

1. *Snow White and the Seven Dwarfs*
2. Mickey Mouse
3. Filling a vat of water
4. James Mason
5. Dodie Smith
6. Cruella de Vil
7. He can fly
8. Mary Poppins
9. Italy
10. Jiminy Cricket
11. Flower
12. John Mills
13. Herbie
14. Simba
15. *The Aristocats*
16. Angela Lansbury
17. St Bernard
18. King Arthur's
19. *Lady and the Tramp*
20. She always found something to be 'glad' about
21. A fox
22. Fred MacMurray
23. Uncle Remus
24. Shrank the kids
25. Jules Verne

Famous Folk • Writers and Poets

1. Keats
2. *The Old Man and the Sea*
3. Australia
4. John Osborne
5. Coleridge
6. D.H. Lawrence
7. *Kim*
8. Katherine Mansfield
9. Tennyson
10. Stream of consciousness
11. Emily Brontë
12. *Old Possum's*
13. *Hamlet*
14. *The Gulag Archipelago*
15. Emily Dickinson
16. *The Grapes of Wrath*
17. Horror
18. Shelley
19. Henrik Ibsen
20. George Gordon
21. Civil Rights
22. *A Tale of Two Cities*
23. Oscar Wilde
24. F. Scott Fitzgerald
25. *Twelfth Night*

Sport and Leisure • Golf

1. Bogey
2. True
3. US Professional Golfers Association Championship
4. Grand Slam
5. It is by invitation only
6. 17
7. Trap
8. Fade
9. 1986
10. Fore
11. Four, five and six
12. Three strokes below par on a hole
13. A double eagle
14. Byron Nelson
15. False
16. Putting on the green
17. Patricia Bradley
18. Pin
19. Seven, eight and nine
20. Zimbabwe
21. Palmer's charges
22. One stroke below par on a hole
23. Jack Nicklaus
24. Practice balls
25. A bandit

Pot Luck

1. Oxfordshire
2. Books of the Bible
3. North Sea
4. *The Jewel in the Crown*
5. *The Hunter*
6. A large gong
7. Mozart
8. Tom Keating
9. Edgar Rice Burroughs
10. Great Dane
11. Virgin Mary
12. Reykjavik
13. Neil Simon
14. *The Poseidon Adventure*
15. Realtors
16. Alec Waugh
17. The fisherman's ring
18. A fish
19. Palomino
20. Corona
21. A piece of music imitating another composer's style
22. Meteorite
23. Marco Polo
24. Stairs
25. MBE

1. The Costa Dorada is a well-known Spanish holiday destination. What does the name mean?

2. Barbados is a volcanic island. True or false?

3. Which fashionable US town appointed Bob Hope as honorary mayor?

4. On which Greek island would you find the late Minoan palace of Knossos?

5. Where would you find the resorts of Albufeira, Praia da Rocha and Lagos?

6. Which English county, popular with holidaymakers, was the setting for the novels of Daphne du Maurier?

7. Name the US state famous for its surfing and its volcanoes.

8. The Canary Islands were once known by what pretty name?

9. Fjordland National Park is an area of great beauty on New Zealand's South Island. What is the jewel of the park, called the 'eighth wonder of the world' by Rudyard Kipling?

10. Niagara Falls has always been a favourite honeymoon spot. Which actress starred in the 1953 film *Niagara*?

11. In 1974 the Turkish invasion divided the island of Cyprus. Which half of the island is Greek?

12. The beautiful French resort of Nice holds a large-scale and very colourful carnival each year. When does it take place?

13. Bali is a favourite holiday destination for Australians and many other nationalities. When is the dry season?

14. The island of Elephantine, so called because it was once an ivory trading post, stands in the Nile opposite which Egyptian city?

15. Ibiza is part of which island group?

16. In which part of France would you find the cathedrals of Rouen and Bayeux?

17. The modern name for Ceylon means 'resplendent land'. What is it?

18. Which Brazilian city is overlooked by Christ the Redeemer at Corcovado?

19. One of Queensland's major tourist attractions gives visitors the opportunity to explore coral reefs by scuba-diving, snorkelling and glass-bottomed boats. What is this attraction called?

20. To which island did Gracie Fields retire?

21. The Maldives is an independent republic of almost 2000 tiny coral islands in which ocean?

22. In Disneyworld's Magic Kingdom in Florida, which of the park's 'lands' is entered through Cinderella's Castle?

23. In which country would you find the Masai Mara game reserve?

24. In which US state would you visit national parks called the Arches, Canyonlands and Bryce Canyon?

25. The ski resort of St Moritz stands on the southern side of which mountain range?

1. What was Kojak's first name?

2. Name the author played by Angela Lansbury in *Murder She Wrote*.

3. Who wrote about the pipe-smoking detective Maigret?

4. Lord Peter Wimsey was created by Dorothy L. Sayers. Whom did he marry?

5. What type of car did Columbo drive?

6. Which instrument did Sherlock Holmes play?

7. Amateur sleuth Brother Cadfael was a 12th-century Welsh monk. Who played him in the TV series?

8. Where did Rockford keep his gun?

9. Sharon Gless was the third actress to play Christine Cagney in *Cagney and Lacey*. Who was the first?

10. Who is the San Franciscan private eye in Dashiell Hammett's *The Maltese Falcon*?

11. Adam Dalgleish is a Scotland Yard detective in whose crime novels?

12. Which girl detective whose father was a former district attorney was created by Edward Stratemeyer?

13. Name the actor, later a star of *Dynasty*, who was the voice of the unseen Charlie in *Charlie's Angels*.

14. What was the nationality of Ngaio Marsh, who often set her work in an English country house?

15. Who was Sexton Blake's boy assistant?

16. What is Miss Marple's first name?

17. In which village does Miss Marple live?

18. Name the author who first wrote about detective Philip Marlowe in *The Big Sleep*.

19. Which actor was the most famous screen Marlowe in *The Big Sleep* in 1946?

20. Agatha Christie created which detective with waxed moustache and 'patent-leather hair'?

21. Name the bumbling detective played by Peter Sellers in *The Pink Panther*.

22 Which fat detective did William Conrad play in the TV series?

23. Who is the modest Roman Catholic priest created by G. K. Chesterton and now the star of a TV series?

24. Barry Foster played Van der Valk in the TV series of that name. In which city did Van der Valk operate?

25. The exploits of comic strip hero Dick Tracy were brought to the screen in the 1990 film. Who played Tracy?

5. In a Spanish bar, what are tapas?

6. Zuppa pavese is an Italian consommé. What would it contain in addition to the basic soup?

7. What is hummus?

8. If a dish you order contains tofu, what would you expect to be eating?

9. Paupiettes are slices of meat or fish prepared in what way?

10. The Japanese call it kanten, other eastern countries call it agar-agar. What is it?

11. What type of beef or lamb is used in keema curry?

12. On a French menu, what name would be given to poached eggs in individual flat dishes with Hollandaise sauce?

13. Calamari are eaten in large quantities in Italy. What is the English name?

14. In Greece or Turkey, rolls of savoury rice wrapped in vine leaves are a popular starter. What are they called?

15. You might finish a meal in Turkey with a cup of sweet coffee and delicious loucoumi. What would you be eating?

16. In an American restaurant, if you asked for a dish to be cooked 'over easy', what would the dish be?

1. In a Mexican restaurant, what name is given to crisp maize pancakes stuffed with meat and salad, with a tasty topping?

2. What is a poussin?

3. The Austrian sachertorte took its name from the chef Franz Sacher. What is it?

4. Bhoona is the Hindi term for cooking spice in hot oil. What does the term bargar mean?

17. What would you expect to find in abundance in an Indian dish described as 'do-piaza'?

18. If an item of food is described as 'au naturel', how is it cooked?

19. The Indonesian dish gado-gado is a vegetable salad with dressing. What is the main ingredient of the dressing?

20. If you ordered pasta with 'supo di carne', what type of sauce would you expect?

21. Usually served in soup or as an entrée, what are quenelles?

22. What is abalone?

23. Lamingtons were named after a Governor of Queensland. What are they?

24. What name is given to herrings salted whole, then smoked?

25. Yams are used a good deal in West Indian cooking. What type of food are they?

1. In Germany, the Federal President is the head of state. What title is held by the head of government?

2. What do the letters ERM stand for?

3. Which party did George Bush belong to?

4. In which country were Five Year Plans the basis of economic planning after 1928?

5. Who founded the fascist party in Italy in 1919?

6. In which city is the headquarters of the European Commission of Human Rights?

7. What French term describes the forcible takeover of government by elements within the country?

8. In which year does China take control of Hong Kong?

9. To which party does Australian leader Bob Hawke, who first won power in 1983, belong?

10. In 1984, Indian troops were sent into which temple to dislodge a Sikh extremist leader?

11. What was the aim of the July Plot, hatched in 1944?

12. Milton Obote was president of which country?

13. Konrad Adenauer was Chancellor of West Germany from 1949 to 1963. Which party did he belong to?

14. The first-ever meeting between a reigning British monarch and a serving US President took place in 1918. Who was the President?

15. What name is given to the referral of proposed legislation to a direct vote by the electorate?

16. What was the subject of the Beveridge Report of 1942 in Britain?

17. Who launched the Cultural Revolution in China?

18. Which country had Jan Christian Smuts as premier between 1939 and 1948?

19. Where does the International Monetary Fund, an agency of the United Nations, have its headquarters?

20. What name is given to the military rulers of the country after an army takeover?

21. In the US, who was meant to benefit from 'affirmative action'?

22. Who suffered under the Cat and Mouse Act in England in the early part of this century?

23. Who was the prime minister of the Vichy government in France during World War II?

24. In which country is the financial clique called 'zaibatsu'?

25. Which British Prime Minister introduced the 'social contract' with the trade unions?

Q13

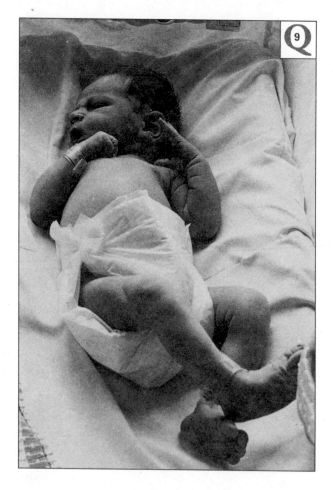

Q9

4. Sometimes a baby is born with one or two of its first teeth already present. True or false?

5. What name is given to the jealousy sometimes shown towards a new baby by an older brother or sister?

6. At what stage in pregnancy does a mother begin to feel the baby's movements?

7. What attaches the baby to the placenta?

8. There are two types of sex chromosome, X and Y. Males have one X and one Y chromosome. What do females have?

9. Roughly how many hours a day does a baby normally sleep during the first three months?

10. What name is given to the tiny telescope mounted on the end of a hollow needle which doctors can pass through the abdomen into the uterus to check on the health of an unborn baby?

11. Modern researchers advise that babies should be put to sleep in what position?

12. Some babies suck their thumbs before they are born. True or false?

13. Which does a baby learn to do first, roll from his front on to his back or from his back on to his stomach?

1. Which doctors specialize in the care of pregnant women?

2. What name is given to the fluid, rich in antibodies, that precedes breast milk?

3. In a developing foetus, which organ makes blood cells?

14. What is the soft spot on the top of a baby's head called?

15. As babies develop in the uterus, their bodies are covered by fine, downy hair, which usually disappears before they are born. What is this hair called?

16. During the first week of life, most babies lose weight. When will they have regained their birth weight?

17. Over the first few weeks, babies learn to focus their eyes. At first, they can only see things clearly about what distance from their faces?

18. What is 'intra-partum care'?

19. Identical twins are formed if a fertilized egg divides in two parts and each half grows into a baby. How are fraternal twins formed?

20. Why might a baby be fed on soya milk?

21. What painful condition sometimes occurs in children up to three months of age, usually late in the day and lasting for only a short time?

22. A triple immunization often given to babies at two to three months of age is known as DTP. What does that stand for?

23. For what condition might a baby might be given phototherapy, during which it lies naked under a fluorescent light?

24. What is the purpose of amniocentesis during pregancy?

25. Some babies, especially those with low birth weight, stop breathing for very brief periods during sleep. What is this called?

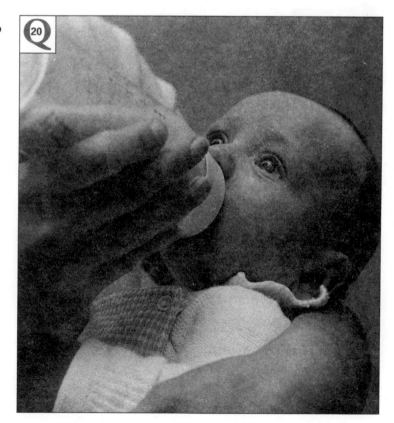

1. In 1988, who was the first woman since Margaret Court to win the tennis Grand Slam?

2. Who won two Olympic marathon titles – one barefoot, the other in shoes?

3. Which Nobel Prize winner wrote *For Whom the Bell Tolls* and *In Our Time*?

4. In which film did Bogart win his only Oscar?

5. Who was the only British Prime Minister this century to win three consecutive general elections?

6. Poet and essayist Octavio Paz won the Nobel Prize for literature in 1990. What nationality is he?

7. Which baseball team has won most World Series?

8. Who was the only world heavyweight boxing champion to remain undefeated throughout his entire professional career?

9. For which film did Dustin Hoffman win an Oscar, *The Graduate* or *Kramer v. Kramer*?

10. Linus Pauling was the only man to win two individual Nobel Prizes. What were they for?

11. Jodie Foster won an Oscar for *Silence of the Lambs* in 1992. For which film did she win it in 1989?

12. Which Belgian cyclist, nicknamed 'the Cannibal', won the Tour de France five times between 1969 and 1974?

Q 11

13. Who won five Olympic golds in athletics in 1924?

14. Apart from the USA, only two countries have ever won the Olympic basketball championship. Which countries were they?

15. To whom is the Lawrence Trophy awarded annually?

16. Which grand-slam winning tennis player was nicknamed 'the Rocket'?

17. For which two films did Glenda Jackson win the Oscar for best actress?

18. Which author of *Lord of the Flies* and *Rites of Passage* won a Nobel Prize for literature in 1983?

19. Koichi Nakono won a record number of titles in which sport?

20. The 1994 Nobel Prize for Peace was awarded to Shimon Peres, Yasser Arafat and which other recipient?

21. At the Barcelona Olympics in 1992, who was the first British woman to win an Olympic track event since 1964?

22. For which film did Clint Eastwood receive an Oscar for best director in 1993?

23. Which member of the British royal family was once elected Sports Personality of the Year?

24. Holly Hunter won an Oscar for her role in which 1994 film?

25. Which of the following won the Nobel Peace Prize: Mikhail Gorbachev, Mother Teresa, Henry Kissinger, Willy Brandt?

5. If you were whipping a rope, what would you be doing?

6. Which small sailing dinghy would be ideal for young beginners?

7. Which is the largest boat in Olympic competition?

8. The first sailor to circumnavigate the world alone was Captain Joshua Slocum, who set off from Rhode Island in 1895. How long did it take him?

9. What are Bruce, Danforth and Meon?

10. In canoeing, speed racing takes place on still water. On what type of water does slalom racing take place?

11. The international phonic alphabet is used in radio signalling for clarity. A is Alpha, B is Bravo. What is Y?

12. In the phonic alphabet, what is O?

13. Under which two bridges does the Oxford and Cambridge University Boat race pass?

14. What are halyards used for?

15. How long has yachting been an official Olympic sport?

16. Which boat skippered jointly by Robin Knox-Johnstone and Peter Blake broke the non-stop round the world record by five days in 1994?

1. What name is given to a light three-cornered headsail used to improve downwind performance?

2. How often does the Whitbread Round the World race take place?

3. What are the fastest sailing boats?

4. Who was the first woman to cross the Atlantic alone, in 1903?

17. The hull of the boat above the waterline is called what?

18. The tall sailing ship built in Germany as the *Horst Wessel* and confiscated after the war became the flagship of the US Coast Guard. What was it named?

19. What, in the world of sailing, is the IYRU?

20. Which British politican captained the winning team in the yacht *Morning Cloud* in the 1969 Sydney to Hobart Race?

21. In the international code of flag signals, what does a yellow flag with a black spot in the centre mean?

22. In 1905 the schooner *Atlantic* set a transatlantic racing record of 12 days 4 hours which was unbroken for 75 years. Who was the skipper?

23. Who was the Australian skipper who wrested the America's Cup from the US, after what seemed like an interminable run of wins, in 1983?

24. In a dinghy or small boat, what would you do with a thwart?

25. On which day of the year does the Sydney to Hobart Race begin?

1. What name is given to the study of the history of words?

2. In Italian cooking, what name is given to small dumplings made of mashed potato?

3. On which Hebridean island is Fingal's Cave?

4. Who dueted with Barbra Streisand in 'You Don't Bring Me Flowers'?

5. In the rhyme, how was Jack's head dressed after he fell down the hill?

6. What would you find in an arboretum?

7. Which country is often called 'the Emerald Isle'?

8. The songs 'My Funny Valentine' and 'The Lady is a Tramp' come from which musical?

9. Name the smallest planet in the solar system.

10. What name is given to a group of elk?

11. The bright spots of sunlight seen around the edge of the moon for a few seconds before and after an eclipse of the sun are called what?

12. What is agronomy?

13. What nationality was the painter El Greco?

Q4

14. If you made a tactless remark or a social error it might be described by which French expression?

15. Which state of Australia has the largest population?

16. What is called the 'fourth estate'?

17. In which country was the film *A Bridge Too Far* set?

18. Who said 'Russia is a riddle wrapped in a mystery inside an enigma'?

19. 'Decimate' is a word often used in an exaggerated sense. What does it actually mean?

20. Methuselah was a character in the Bible but in modern times methuselahs are containers for what?

21. Who painted *The Laughing Cavalier*?

22. The cocktail called Rusty Nail contains whisky and which liqueur?

23. What is a glockenspiel?

24. Who played the cabaret entertainer in *The Blue Angel*?

25. Which singer was nicknamed 'the last of the red-hot mamas'?

Geography and Travel • Holiday Spots

1. Golden coast
2. False
3. Palm Springs
4. Crete
5. Algarve, Portugal
6. Cornwall
7. Hawaii
8. Blessed or Fortunate Isles
9. Milford Sound
10. Marilyn Monroe
11. The south
12. The fortnight
    before Lent
13. May to November
14. Aswan
15. Balearics
16. Normandy
17. Sri Lanka
18. Rio de Janeiro
19. Great Barrier Reef
20. Capri
21. Indian
22. Fantasyland
23. Kenya
24. Utah
25. The Alps

Popular Culture • Detectives

1. Theo
2. Jessica Fletcher
3. Georges Simenon
4. Harriet Vane
5. Peugeot 403 Cabriolet
6. Violin
7. Derek Jacobi
8. In a cookie jar
9. Loretta Swit
10. Sam Spade
11. P. D. James's
12. Nancy Drew
13. John Forsythe
14. New Zealander
15. Tinker
16. Jane
17. St Mary Mead
18. Raymond Chandler
19. Humphrey Bogart
20. Hercule Poirot
21. Inspector Clouseau
22. Cannon
23. Father Brown
24. Amsterdam
25. Warren Beatty

Indoors and Out • Menumaster

1. Tacos
2. Baby chicken
3. Rich chocolate cake
4. Frying whole spices
5. Snacks served with a drink
6. A whole egg and toast covered with cheese and grilled
7. Chick-pea paste
8. Bean curd
9. Rolled and stuffed
10. A type of seaweed
11. Mince
12. Oeufs Bénédictine
13. Squid
14. Dolmades
15. Turkish delight
16. Fried eggs
17. Onion
18. It is uncooked
19. Peanuts
20. Meat sauce
21. A very light dumpling
22. A kind of shellfish
23. Chocolate cakes
24. Bloaters
25. Root vegetables

Past and Present • Political Affairs

1. Federal Chancellor
2. Exchange Rate Mechanism
3. Republican
4. USSR
5. Mussolini
6. Strasbourg
7. Coup d'état
8. 1997
9. Labour
10. Golden Temple at Amritsar
11. Assassination of Hitler
12. Uganda
13. Christian Democrat
14. Woodrow Wilson
15. Referendum
16. Social Security
17. Mao Ze Dong
18. South Africa
19. Washington DC, USA
20. Junta
21. Members of minority ethnic groups
22. Suffragettes
23. Henri Pétain
24. Japan
25. Harold Wilson

Youth World • Babycare

1. Obstetricians
2. Colostrum
3. Liver
4. True
5. Sibling rivalry
6. 18 to 22 weeks
7. Umbilical cord
8. Two X chromosomes
9. 14 to 18 hours
10. Fetoscope
11. On their backs
12. True
13. From front to back
14. Fontanelle
15. Lanugo
16. At about 10 days old
17. 20cm (8in)
18. Care given during labour and delivery
19. Two eggs are shed from the ovary and fertilized simultaneously
20. If he is allergic to cows' milk
21. Colic
22. Diphtheria, tetanus and pertussis
23. Jaundice
24. To check for genetic and developmental disorders
25. Apnoea

Famous Folk • Winners

1. Steffi Graf
2. Abebe Bikila
3. Ernest Hemingway
4. *The African Queen*
5. Margaret Thatcher
6. Mexican
7. New York Yankees
8. Rocky Marciano
9. *Kramer v. Kramer*
10. Chemistry and Peace
11. *The Accused*
12. Eddie Merckx
13. Paavo Nurmi
14. USSR and Yugoslavia
15. Scorer of the fastest first class cricket century
16. Rod Laver
17. *Women in Love* and *A Touch of Class*
18. William Golding
19. Cycling
20. Yitzak Rabin
21. Sally Gunnell
22. *Unforgiven*
23. The Princess Royal
24. *The Piano*
25. All of them

Sport and Leisure • Boats and Sailing

1. Spinnaker
2. Every four years
3. Catamarans
4. Gladys Gradeley
5. Binding the end to stop fraying
6. A pram dinghy
7. Soling
8. Three years
9. Anchors
10. Wild water
11. Yankee
12. Oscar
13. Hammersmith and Barnes
14. Hoisting sails
15. Since 1908
16. *ENZA New Zealand*
17. Topsides
18. *Eagle*
19. International Yacht Racing Union
20. Edward Heath
21. Altering course to port
22. Charlie Barr
23. John Bertrand
24. Sit on it
25. Boxing Day

Pot Luck

1. Etymology
2. Gnocchi
3. Staffa
4. Neil Diamond
5. With vinegar and brown paper
6. Trees
7. Ireland
8. *Pal Joey*
9. Pluto
10. Gang
11. Baily's beads
12. The study of crops and
    soils
13. Greek
14. Faux pas
15. New South Wales
16. The Press
17. Holland
18. Winston Churchill
19. To reduce by one-tenth
20. Champagne
21. Frans Hals
22. Drambuie
23. A musical instrument
24. Marlene Dietrich
25. Sophie Tucker

Q 5

1. Which French river is famed for the châteaux in its valley?

2. In which river are the 'thousand islands'?

3. What is the longest river in Australia?

4. The source of the Nile was a mystery for centuries. Now it is known to be two rivers, which unite at Khartoum. What are they called?

5. On which river does the city of Vienna stand?

6. What name is given to a flat stretch of land within a river valley, which is the remnant of an earlier flood plain, when the river was at a higher level?

7. The Rio Grande river forms part of the international boundary between the US and which country?

8. In which river was Jesus baptized?

9. Name the river that rises on the Tibetan Plateau of western China and has flooded more often and killed more people than any other.

10. Which river has the largest delta?

11. What is a delta?

12. How many rivers are there in Saudi Arabia?

13. Tower Bridge, over the River Thames, was opened in 1894. What makes it unique among London's bridges?

14. Which gulf does the Mississippi flow into?

15. In which country does the Zambezi River reach the sea?

16. What, in a river, is a meander?

17. The River Zambezi flows across the savannah of Zambia before plunging down Africa's most spectacular falls. What are they called?

18. On which American river is the Hoover Dam?

19. The Pied Piper of Hamelin cured the town's plague of rats by leading them into which river?

20. In which country is the River Po?

21. Which sea does the Nile flow into?

22. Francisco de Orellana explored it from Quito in Ecuador to the Atlantic in 1542 and called it the Rio Mar. By what name is it known now?

23. The third longest river in the world, the Yangtze in China, is famous for what spectacular features?

24. Which Canadian river rises in the Rockies as the Athabaska, leaves the Athabaska Lake as the Slave River, then changes its name as it leaves the Great Slave Lake?

25. The Ponte Vecchio in Florence was the only bridge over which river until 1218?

1. Whose autobiography is *A Long Walk to Freedom*?

2. To which genre do the novels of Zane Grey belong?

3. Which Jacqueline Susann novel sold nearly seven million copies in the first six months after its publication in 1966?

Q 25

4. In which John Le Carré novel does George Smiley appear for the first time?

5. What story is told in *Exodus* by Leon Uris?

6. Two of the books in the Dollanganger series, by Virginia Andrews, are *Petals in the Wind* and *If There Be Thorns*. What is the first book?

7. Which novel brought Salman Rushdie a death sentence from Islam?

8. Name the most famous book written by Grace Metalious.

9. Which popular US novelist, with a string of best-sellers to her credit, is a descendant of the Lowenbrau brewery family and ran a PR firm called 'Supergirls' before becoming a novelist?

10. Stephen King's book *Misery* is about a writer who falls into the hands of his crazy number one fan. Who stars in the film with James Caan?

11. Which novel by Frederick Forsyth tells of an assassination attempt on Charles de Gaulle?

12. Who wrote *Saturday Night and Sunday Morning* and *Loneliness of the Long Distance Runner*?

13. In *Lolita* by Vladimir Nabokov, middle-aged Humbert Humbert lusts after the nymphet Lolita. How old is she?

14. Louisa May Alcott's *Little Women* concerns which New England family?

15. Germaine Greer is the author of the classic feminist work *The Female Eunuch*. What is her native country?

16. Which novel by Jeffrey Archer follows the fortunes of four MPs over 30 years from the time they take their seats in the 1960s?

17. *How to Save Your Own Life* and *Parachutes and Kisses*, by Erica Jong, both feature the same New York heroine. In which novel does her story begin?

18. Name the novel by Harper Lee in which a lawyer in America's deep south defends a negro accused of rape, with the action seen through the eyes of the lawyer's young daughter.

19. Who is the heroine of Barbara Taylor Bradford's *A Woman of Substance*?

Q16

20. *Where Eagles Dare*, by Alistair Maclean, follows a group of commandos sent to rescue an American general held prisoner by the Nazis in a Bavarian castle. In the film, who plays the commando leader?

21. Who wrote about Adrian Mole and about the British royal family living on a council estate?

22. Which Joseph Heller novel, set on a Mediterranean island in World War II, gave a new expression to the language?

23. Which English crime writer created a mystery herself by disappearing for a fortnight in 1926, only to be discovered at a Harrogate hotel?

24. Who caused a furore with his book *Diana: Her True Story* about the Princess of Wales?

25. *The Stud* was a 1978 film based on a book by Jackie Collins and starring her sister Joan. What was the follow-up film in 1979, also based on a Jackie Collins novel?

Q 4

1. In which country would you see the flightless emu in its natural habitat?

2. Which birds are the best known 'nest parasites'?

3. What is the scientific name for butterflies and moths?

4. Robins are known as friendly garden birds in western Europe and the American robin was named by settlers because of its red breast. What type of bird is the American robin?

5. What plant is known as the 'butterfly bush'?

6. Which bird is known for its ability to mimic human speech?

7. What type of bird is a raptor?

8. By what name is the blue peafowl commonly known?

9. How do butterflies extract the flower nectar on which they feed?

10. Where does the wood stork nest?

11. The life-cycle of the butterfly consists of four stages. What are they?

12. Which nocturnal, flightless bird gives a nickname to New Zealanders?

13. Legend says that the British monarchy will fall if which birds leave the Tower of London?

14. The *Hesperiidae* family of butterflies are often called 'skippers'. Why?

15. If a bird was vinaceous, what colour would it be?

16. How many families of butterflies are there?

17. Rooks are gregarious birds and their large twig nests can be seen grouped in tall trees. They often feed in mixed flocks and share communal winter roosts with which birds?

18. In what part of the world would you find butterflies called heliconius mimic, blue-green reflector and Cramer's mesene?

19. What sort of nests do swallows build?

20. How did the mockingbird get its name?

21. On a butterfly, what are eye-spots?

22. What is a cursorial bird?

23. The *Nymphalidae* family of butterflies are often called 'brushfooted butterflies'. Why?

24. What is described as a bird's 'nuptial finery'?

25. Blue-tits and great-tits are favourite garden birds and both are acrobatic feeders. How are great-tits distinguished from blue-tits in appearance?

Q 25

3. In the American War of Independence, the British were surrounded at Yorktown, Virginia in 1781. Who led the American troops?

4. Eleven southern states broke away from the north in 1861 and formed their own union. What was this called?

5. The turning point of the war was the battle of Gettysburg. In which state is Gettysburg?

6. What was Billy the Kid's real name?

7. Who made his 'last stand' against the Sioux Indians in 1876?

8. In the most infamous western gunfight, at the OK Corral, the Earp brothers and Doc Holliday faced and fought the McLowery brothers and members of which other family?

9. Etta Place was the girlfriend of the Sundance Kid. Which actress played Etta in the film *Butch Cassidy and the Sundance Kid*?

10. Which President promised to 'bind up the nation's wounds' after the Civil War?

11. As immigrants poured into America, they were taken to an island in New York harbour for medical checks. Name the island.

12. Who broadcast 'Fireside Chats' to the American people in the 1930s?

1. Where was the first permanent English settlement in 1607?

2. In 1773 colonists boarded ships in Boston harbour, throwing cargo overboard as a protest against British taxes in the Boston Tea Party. What were the colonists disguised as?

16.

17. Where did Shi'ite Muslim fundamentalists hold US embassy staff hostage in 1980?

18. During the Ford administration, George Bush acted as special envoy to which country?

19. In which scandal was Colonel Oliver North involved in 1986?

20. President Clinton was committed to appointing a woman as Attorney General but his first two choices came to grief in what was known as Nannygate. What was the problem in both cases?

21. Why were the rebellious students of the 1960s called the Spock Generation?

22. Which Caribbean island was invaded in 1983?

13. During whose presidency did the Korean war take place?

23. Where was a bombing campaign known as 'Rolling Thunder' carried out in 1965?

14. Where was the Bay of Pigs?

15. In 1960 an American U-2 reconnaissance plane was shot down over the Soviet Union and the pilot was sentenced to ten years imprisonment. Who was he?

24. Who told the Americans in 1961 that his goal was to land a man on the moon by the end of the decade?

25. Name the independent candidate in the 1992 Presidential election.

16. Which president did Jimmy Carter challenge in 1976?

8. Name the world's smallest breed of horse.

9. What is a family of kittens called?

10. Llamas have been domesticated in South America, both as pack animals and for meat, hide and wool. What family do they belong to?

11. Which dog's present name comes from a character in Sir Walter Scott's novel *Guy Mannering*?

12. Which animal is known as sand rat or desert kangaroo?

13. What special purpose was the Tennessee walking horse was bred for in the southern US?

14. What were husky dogs used for in Iceland and Lapland?

1. What is a male guinea pig called?

2. Where does the ragdoll breed of cat originate?

3. Goats can be house-trained. True or false?

4. Which dog is often used as a symbol of Britain?

5. How is the height of a horse measured?

6. What breed of cat is probably directly descended from the cats of ancient Egypt?

7. Which animals might be blue imperial, New Zealand white or angora?

15. Name the animal resulting from the mating of a donkey and a pony, if the sire was the donkey.

16. Toggenburg, Saanan and Anglo-Nubian are types of which animal?

17. Two distinctive breeds of working dog have been developed in Australia. One is known as the Australian cattle dog or Queensland heeler. What is the other?

18. What is the alternative name for the breed of dog known as the Russian wolfhound?

19. What type of animal is a guinea pig?

20. If feline applies to the cat and canine applies to the dog, what word would apply to the horse?

21. Turkish van cats have a natural liking for something most cats loathe. What is it?

22. From which country did the poodle originate?

23. What is a female mouse called?

24. What is unusual about the coat of the Cornish rex cat?

25. Golden hamsters are one of our newest pets. When were they first bred in captivity?

1. St Swithin is honoured on 15 July. If it rains that day, what will happen afterwards?

2. To which order of monks did St Bernard of Clairvaux belong?

3. Name the leader of a murderous 'family' in California who was described by the prosecutor at his trial as 'one of the most evil, satanic men who ever walked the face of the earth'.

4. St Peter was the leader of the Apostles. He was given the name Peter by Jesus. What did it mean?

5. Who is the patron saint of artists and painters?

6. Hitler became Chancellor of Germany in 1933. Where did he address a rally of 200,000 people in September?

7. The carol 'Good King Wenceslas' commemorates the martyr who is patron saint of which country?

8. Who was the Italian founder of the Franciscan order?

9. How long a sentence of imprisonment was passed on David Berkowitz, the notorious 'Son of Sam' who terrorized New York in 1977?

10. In 1858 Saint Bernadette saw visions of the Virgin Mary. How old was Bernadette at the time?

11. With what emblem is St Agnes portrayed?

12. What does the name 'Beelzebub' mean?

13. According to tradition, who wiped the face of Jesus on the way to Calvary?

14. Where was Thomas à Becket murdered?

15. Burke and Hare were 19th-century grave-robbers and murderers and 'to burke' has passed into the language. What does it mean?

16. Who is the patron saint of hopeless causes?

17. St John of the Cross was a Carmelite friar. What was his native country?

18. Dr Marcel Petiot was found guilty of 25 murders and guillotined in France in 1946. What did he pretend to his victims that he was running during World War II?

19. With what emblem is St Peter usually portrayed?

20. The English murderer George Joseph Smith drowned several wives for their insurance money. What were these murders popularly called?

21. Joan of Arc was a peasant girl who led the French army to victory in the 15th century. Which country was France fighting?

22. St Agnes was martyred in Rome and St Agatha in Sicily. What were they both dedicated to defending?

23. Who is the patron saint of cooks?

24. How did St Stephen die?

25. Ronald de Feo slaughtered his family at a Long Island house which later became notorious for terrifying happenings and was the subject of a book and a film. Where was it?

Q 8

1. What are netsuke?

2. Where did the willow pattern on china originate?

3. What kind of porcelain is called 'biscuit'?

4. How many spoons are there in an original set of Apostle spoons?

5. In furniture, what is a davenport?

6. Fabergé was official jeweller to the Russian Imperial court. What did he make specially for the Empress each year from 1884?

7. What is the usual colour of lacquer furniture?

8. In which country were fans invented?

9. If you had a rummer from Germany, what would you do with it?

10. What is scrimshaw?

11. The British call a high chest with seven or nine drawers a tallboy. What is it called in the US?

12. Carriage clocks were first produced as cheap, portable desk clocks in which country?

13. Fairings are popular with collectors. Originally, what were they?

14. In which English county has Wedgwood been produced since 1759?

15. What is a whatnot?

16. Button collecting is a popular hobby, especially in the US. In which century were buttons first worn on clothes?

17. Where does Belleek porcelain come from?

18. What is the name given to a design built up of tiny pieces of veneer?

19. Dutch Delftware is usually what colour?

20. Which country does the long, broad bench called an ottoman come from?

21. Chippendale was a master-craftsman, producing high quality furniture. What was his first name?

Q 21

22. What is a prie-dieu?

23. Louis Quatorze furniture, from the second half of the 18th century, is massive, with ornate decoration. What is this style of furniture usually called?

24. A stick-back is the simplest form of which type of chair?

25. In the US a dumb waiter is a service lift. If you bought an early 19th-century dumb waiter in a saleroom, what would it be?

4. What comedy film earned Oscars for Clark Gable and Claudette Colbert in 1935?

5. Which is the world's largest residential palace?

6. Which game begins with a bully?

7. In what field did Rachel Heyhoe, later Heyhoe-Flint, achieve fame?

8. What would a cook add to a Welsh rarebit to make a buck rarebit?

9. British policemen are sometimes called 'bobbies', after the founder of the Metropolitan Police. Who was he?

10. Where in the US would you find Johns Hopkins university?

11. How many symphonies did Beethoven compose?

12. Which Shakespearean character wore yellow stockings, as the result of a trick?

13. 'True Love' and 'Now You Has Jazz' are songs from which musical?

14. In Canada, what is the RCMP?

15. Marc Chagall painted in a variety of styles, including Cubism. Which was his native country?

16. What nickname was given to Swedish singer Jenny Lind?

1. What would you do with parkin?

2. Name the small independent state set in the High Pyrenees between Spain and France.

3. In *An Englishman Abroad*, which actress meets spy Guy Burgess in Russia?

17. In heraldry, what is the name for red?

18. The characters Petruchio, Bianca and Katharina appear in which Shakespearean comedy?

19. What is the Latin term for 'in the year of our Lord'?

20. Hudson, the butler in *Upstairs, Downstairs*, was rejected for military service. What was his war work?

21. In the US, why would you win an Edgar?

22. What is the French phrase for a pen-name?

23. In which sport is the Stanley Cup awarded?

24. A sackbut is an earlier version of which instrument?

25. What type of car does Edward Woodward drive in *The Equalizer*?

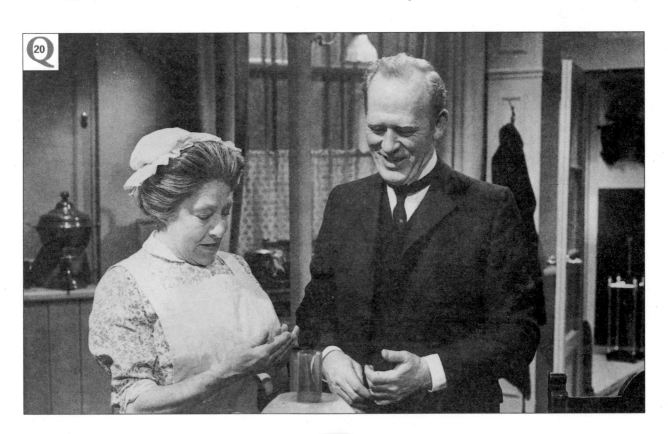

Answers to Quiz 8

Geography and Travel · Rivers

1. Loire
2. St Lawrence
3. Murray River
4. White Nile and Blue Nile
5. Danube
6. River terrace
7. Mexico
8. Jordan
9. Yellow River
10. Ganges
11. An area formed from the sediment deposited
at the mouth of a river
12. None
13. It is the only bridge that opens
14. Gulf of Mexico
15. Mozambique
16. A bend or curve
17. Victoria Falls
18. Colorado
19. Weser
20. Italy
21. Mediterranean
22. Amazon
23. Gorges
24. Mackenzie River
25. River Arno

Popular Culture · Bestsellers

1. Nelson Mandela
2. Westerns
3. *Valley of the Dolls*
4. *The Spy Who Came in From the Cold*
5. The creation of Modern Israel
6. *Flowers in the Attic*
7. *The Satanic Verses*
8. *Peyton Place*
9. Danielle Steel
10. Kathy Bates
11. *The Day of the Jackal*
12. Alan Sillitoe
13. 12
14. The March family
15. Australia
16. *First Among Equals*
17. *Fear of Flying*
18. *To Kill a Mockingbird*
19. Emma Harte
20. Richard Burton
21. Sue Townshend
22. *Catch 22*
23. Agatha Christie
24. Andrew Morton
25. *The Bitch*

Indoors and Out · Birds and Butterflies

1. Australia
2. Cuckoos
3. *Lepidoptera*
4. Thrush
5. Buddleia
6. Hill Mynah
7. A bird of prey
8. Peacock
9. Through a long, hollow feeding tube
10. In a treetop
11. Egg, caterpillar, pupa and adult
12. Kiwi
13. Ravens
14. They dart from flower to flower
15. Wine-coloured
16. Five
17. Jackdaws
18. Central and South America
19. Mud bowls built on to a wall or roof
20. It mimics other birds
21. Circular markings found
on the wings
22. A ground-dwelling species
23. The male's front legs are covered with tufts of scales
24. Breeding plumage
25. By their black and white head pattern and white outer tail feathers

Past and Present · American History

1. Jamestown, Virginia
2. Native Americans
3. George Washington
4. The Confederacy
5. Pennsylvania
6. William Bonney
7. General Custer
8. The Clantons
9. Katharine Ross
10. Abraham Lincoln
11. Ellis Island
12. Franklin D. Roosevelt
13. Harry S. Truman's
14. Cuba
15. Gary Powers
16. Gerald Ford
17. Tehran
18. China
19. Iran-Contra Affair
20. Each had employed an illegal alien as nanny
21. Their behaviour was blamed on the permissive child-raising ideas of Dr Benjamin Spock
22. Grenada
23. Vietnam
24. John F. Kennedy
25. Ross Perot

Youth World · Favourite Animals

1. Boar
2. USA
3. False
4. Bulldog
5. In hands
6. Egyptian mau
7. Rabbits
8. Falabella
9. Litter
10. Camel
11. Dandie Dinmont
12. Gerbil
13. To carry plantation
owners round their vast estates
14. To pull sleds
15. Mule
16. Goat
17. Australian kelpie
18. Borzoi
19. Rodent
20. Equine
21. Water
22. France
23. A doe
24. It is curly or wavy
25. 1930s

Famous Folk · Saints and Sinners

1. It will rain for 40 days
2. Cistercians
3. Charles Manson
4. The rock
5. St Luke
6. Nuremberg
7. Bohemia
8. St Francis of Assissi
9. 365 years
10. 14
11. A lamb
12. Lord of the Flies
13. St Veronica
14. Canterbury Cathedral
15. To murder by suffocation
16. St Jude
17. Spain
18. An escape route for those in danger from the Nazis
19. Keys
20. Brides in the Bath murders
21. England
22. Their virginity
23. St Lawrence
24. He was stoned to death
25. Amityville

Sport and Leisure · Antiques and Collectables

1. Small Japanese carvings in wood or ivory
2. Britain
3. Unglazed porcelain
4. 13
5. A small writing desk with a sloping surface
6. A jewelled Easter egg
7. Black with gold designs
8. Japan
9. Drink from it
10. Decorated or carved
11. Highboy
12. France
13. Small china ornaments won at fairgrounds
14. Staffordshire
15. A tiered stand, used to display trinkets
16. 14th century
17. Northern Ireland
18. Marquetry
19. Blue design on a white background
20. Turkey
21. Thomas
22. A small praying desk with a shelf for the knees and a higher shelf for the prayer book
23. Baroque
24. Windsor
25. A revolving stand with several tiers

Pot Luck

1. Eat it
2. Andorra
3. Coral Browne
4. *It Happened One Night*
5. The Vatican
6. Hockey
7. Cricket
8. A poached egg
9. Sir Robert Peel
10. Baltimore, Maryland
11. Nine
12. Malvolio
13. *High Society*
14. Royal Canadian Mounted Police
15. Russia
16. The Swedish Nightingale
17. Gules
18. *The Taming of the Shrew*
19. *Anno Domini*
20. Special constable
21. For writing a mystery novel
22. *Nom de plume*
23. Ice hockey
24. Trombone
25. Jaguar

1. What gas is released when rainforests burn?

2. What is hydropower?

3. In which country did 'Operation Tiger' begin, with the object of creating nature reserves for tigers?

4. Where was the world's largest oil spill?

5. What provides the entire diet of the endangered giant panda?

6. In 1961 an international organization was established to raise funds for conservation. Its first name was the World Wildlife Fund. What is it called now?

7. Which synthetic chemical, damaging to the environment, is still used in aerosol cans and in refrigerators?

8. What name is given to the heating up of the earth's atmospheric temperature?

9. In 1986 an accident at a nuclear power station in the USSR caused widespread contamination. Where did it happen?

10. What type of wood are teak and mahogany?

11. The snow leopard has been hunted for its spectacular coat, which is frosty-grey with dark rosettes. It is seldom seen but where is its habitat?

12. The power from burning wood and plant material is called what?

13. Which gas is produced from the rotting of household rubbish dumped on landfill sites?

14. The number of rhinos has been dramatically reduced because their horn is so highly prized in the Far East. What is it used for?

15. What name is given to the region in the stratosphere that absorbs the sun's ultra-violet rays and protects humans from its harmful effects?

16. Which substance produced in nuclear reactors can be used to make nuclear weapons?

17. Right whales were killed in such large numbers that they are now rare. How did they get their name?

18. What is the device for cutting the toxic fumes from car exhausts called?

19. Name the political party that grew up in Western Europe in the 1970s with conservation as its main aim.

20. Materials like glass, plastic and heavy metals are nonbiodegradable. What does this mean?

21. Which endangered animals inhabit the forests of the Virunga range of extinct volcanoes along the borders of Zaire, Rwanda and Uganda?

22. What metal is used to create nuclear power?

Q21

23. *Waldsterben* is the German name given to tree dieback due to air pollution, which was first noticed in the Black Forest in the late 1970s. What does the name mean?

24. The California condor is on the verge of extinction. What type of bird is it?

25. In 1979 a pressurized water reactor leaked radioactivity in the US. Where did this happen?

1. Who worked as a shop assistant, became an award-winning actress and then a British MP?

2. In which sport did Johnny Weissmuller win five Olympic gold medals before becoming Tarzan?

3. Which American astronaut became a US senator in 1974 but was unsuccessful in his bid to become a Democratic presidential candidate?

4. Before he studied medicine, what was Albert Schweitzer's occupation?

5. Which former *Neighbours* star had a 1992 hit with *Give Me Just a Little More Time*?

6. In which profession did Golda Meir, Israeli Prime Minister from 1969 to 1974, originally train?

7. Oliver Reed was once a bouncer for a strip club. True or false?

8. In which field did former actress Sheila Scott find fame in 1966?

9. Who played Walter Mitty and Hans Andersen, then went on to become Ambassador-at-Large for UNICEF?

10. What was Ernest Hemingway's job before he became a novelist?

11. Clint Eastwood became mayor of which American town?

12. Which member of the Monty Python comedy team wrote *Families and How To Survive Them* with Robin Skynner?

13. What was US President Hoover's original profession?

14. Which film actress became Minister of Culture in Greece?

15. What was Cleo Laine's job when she first met Johnny Dankworth?

16. Edward Woodward plays *The Equalizer*. What secret agent character did he play 18 years earlier, in another series?

17. Austrian motor-racing world champion Niki Lauda retired in 1985 to concentrate on his own business. What is it?

18. Ray Reardon and Christopher Dean both worked in the same job before they became snooker and ice dance stars respectively. What were they?

19. Who was a sports commentator, then a film actor, and later one of the leaders of the world?

20. Who began her film career playing Celie, a teenage bride in the deep south of America, and appeared as a singing 'nun' in two more recent films?

21. A US comedienne sometimes called 'the bitchiest woman in comedy', whose autobiography is entitled *Enter Talking*, won an Emmy for her talk show in 1990. Who is she?

22. What was Sir Walter Scott's original profession?

23. Neil Armstrong was the first man to walk on the moon. In 1971 he left NASA to do what?

24. Samuel Langhorne Clemens had several jobs before becoming famous as Mark Twain the novelist. Which job provided him with his pseudonym?

25. Who was Harry Palmer, and Alfie, and taught Rita a few things?

Q16

7. The part of a snail's body that remains inside the shell is protected by a thick skin. What is it called?

8. Aphids and leafhoppers are both a menace not only because they feed on plants but because they exude 'honey dew'. What does this encourage?

9. Are booklice really found in books?

10. Which is the most widely spread land bird in the world, found on every continent but Antarctica, and welcome because it preys on mice and voles?

11. Where does the scorpion carry its sting?

1. The 14th-century Black Death was brought to Europe by the fleas on which type of rat?

2. The boll weevil is the chief threat to which crop?

3. Why are earthworms the gardener's friends?

4. What is the only carnivore native to Australia?

5. In which country is the hedgehog considered sacred?

6. The house mouse is a prolific breeder. How many litters can it produce in a year?

12. Tigers will usually prey on animals like deer, antelope and monkey but they will sometimes raid villages in search of a a particularly tasty prey. What is it?

13. Mink are farmed for their fur but in the wild they often prey on poultry. What family do mink belong to?

14. Why is the vole a threat to trees and shrubs?

15. Which mosquitoes suck blood, the males or females?

16. Which creature is known for spoiling lawns with its burrowing habits?

17. The raccoon often steals fruit and vegetables from farmers. What name is given to the raccoon's home?

18. The caterpillar of which butterfly, common in Europe, the Mediterranean and North Africa, strips the leaves of the brassica family?

19. What are the two best-known types of blow-flies?

20. How do polecats mark their territory?

21. What do Americans call the poisonous spider known in Australia as the redback and in New Zealand as the katipo?

22. Which North American rodent, disliked by farmers, lives in large 'towns' with complicated patterns of interconnecting tunnels?

23. The wolverine, sometimes known as the skunk-bear or carijou, has another name that reflects its enormous appetite. What is it?

24. The mongoose can be a menace to birds and other wildlife in its natural habitat, but it is useful for what particular ability?

25. Where did the grey squirrel originally come from?

Q 9

4. In which Dublin park were Lord Frederick Cavendish, chief secretary for Ireland, and his under-secretary T. H. Burke murdered in 1882?

5. Which organization was founded by Michael Collins in 1919?

6. In 1937 the Irish Free State changed its name to what?

7. What is the Republic of Ireland's lower chamber of parliament called?

8. Which organization has a name that means 'Ourselves Alone'?

1. Which British Prime Minister decided that the Union, the joining of English and Irish parliaments, was the answer to Ireland's problems?

2. What was the reason for the 1845 famine in Ireland?

3. What name was given to the rising of April 1916, when nationalists seized Dublin post office and proclaimed a republic?

9. Mairead Corrigan and Betty Williams founded which movement in 1976?

10. What are Fianna Fáil and Fine Gael?

11. How did Bobby Sands and Francis Hughes die in 1981?

12. Northern Ireland is divided into how many counties?

15. In the 1920s a special auxiliary force of the Royal Irish constabulary was employed by the British to combat Irish nationalists. Their popular name came from the colour of their uniforms. What was it?

16. The 'Guildford Four', who had been convicted of terrorist acts, were released when the Court of Appeal found their convictions unsound. How long had they served in prison?

17. Two years after the release of the 'Guildford Four', another group was released after a decision of the Court of Appeal. By what name were they popularly known?

18. Which war hero and member of the British royal family was killed by the IRA in 1979?

19. What do the initials INLA stand for?

20. Which US President visited Ireland in 1963?

21. Which famous London store was bombed in 1983?

22. The Anglo-Irish agreement of 1985 was much criticized. What did it promise Unionists about the status of Northern Ireland?

13. In which year were British troops deployed in Northern Ireland to maintain law and order?

14. What name is given to the civil rights disorders in Northern Ireland?

23. 1984 saw an attempt to kill members of the UK cabinet during the Conservative Party conference. In which town did this happen?

24. Who is the President of Sinn Fein?

25. What party does Ian Paisley lead?

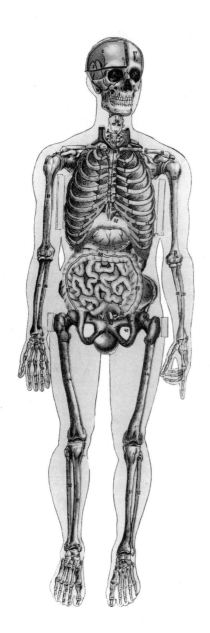

1. How many teeth are there in the first set, the 'milk' teeth?

2. The second set of teeth start coming through when a child is six or seven. How many teeth are there in this set?

3. A baby girl is born with thousands of egg cells in her ovaries. True or false?

4. What name is used for people who can use either hand equally well?

5. Where are the radius and the ulna?

6. What percentage of body weight do muscles account for?

7. Do arteries take blood away from the heart or to the heart?

8. What is produced by some white cells to kill disease organisms?

9. Which hormone controls a man's masculine appearance?

10. Is colour blindness more common in men or women?

11. How many bones make up the vertebral column?

12. The normal pulse rate for a baby is 120 beats per minute. How many beats is it in an adult?

13. If puberty occurs before the age of 10 in a boy, what is it called?

14. What type of joint is the hip?

15. Girls usually stop growing by the age of 16 or 17. What age do boys normally stop growing?

16. What kind of acid, found in the stomach, dissolves food ready for digestion?

17. Where is the thyroid gland situated?

18. The rate at which the body uses up energy is called what?

19. Which part of the blood carries hormones around the body?

20. What is the first part of the small intestine called?

21. Are girls or boys more likely to be left-handed?

22. What is the smallest bone in the ear?

23. Give the common name for the clavicle.

24. A baby starts life with 300 bones. How many will it have as an adult?

25. What is the epidermis?

1. Name the young woman who loses her reason and drowns herself in *Hamlet*.

2. In *The Wizard of Oz*, who are the two wicked witches?

3. What is the first name of TV's Inspector Morse?

4. What is 'Crocodile' Dundee's first name?

5. When Clark Kent turns into his alter ego Superman, which reporter falls in love with him?

6. Who is the little boy who never grew up?

7. Arthur Daley's second minder is his nephew Ray. Who was the first minder?

8. Who saw Cock Robin die?

9. What is the problem with Cyrano de Bergerac's appearance?

10. Clara Peggotty is nurse to which young Dickens character?

11. In *Alice in Wonderland*, the Mad Hatter pours hot tea over which small companion?

12. Which couple war in the 1989 film directed by Danny De Vito and starring Michael Douglas and Kathleen Turner?

13. Who is the famous sidekick of Sherlock Holmes?

14. Who is Lady Chatterley's gamekeeper lover?

15. In *Citizen Kane*, what is Charles Foster Kane's newspaper?

16. What is the name of the nightclub singer in the play *I Am a Camera* and the film *Cabaret*?

17. In Beatrix Potter's books, what did Ginger and Pickles do until they were no longer able to pay the bills?

18. When Robin Hood becomes a titled gentleman, what is he called?

19. What is Just William's surname?

20. What is the profession of Indiana Jones?

21. Who is Phileas Fogg's servant who travels with him in *Round the World in Eighty Days*?

22. Holden Caulfield is a lonely, sensitive 16-year-old who leaves home in which novel by J. D. Salinger?

23. Joanna Lumley plays which part in *The New Avengers*?

24. In *Washington Behind Closed Doors*, what is the name of the President, played by Jason Robards?

25. Name the semi-autobiographical play by Eugene O'Neill which tells the story of a troubled family where the mother is a drug addict, her husband is an ageing former matinée idol, one of her sons is a drunk and the other is dying of consumption.

Q 15

1. Who wrote the music for the Diaghilev ballets *The Firebird* and *Petrushka*?

2. Which opera was commissioned to celebrate the opening of the Suez Canal?

3. Singer Joan Sutherland is one of the best-known names in opera. Which country does she come from?

4. Which opera house is found in New York's Lincoln Center?

5. In which ballet does the leading ballerina dance the role of Odette-Odile?

6. What is the lowest female singing voice?

7. Name the Swiss hero featured in an opera by Rossini, first performed in 1829.

8. Benjamin Britten wrote the opera *Billy Budd*. Who starred as Billy in the film of the same name?

9. The fourth and last part of Wagner's Ring Cycle is called *Götterdämmerung*. What is its English name?

10. How many basic foot positions are there in ballet?

11. Who founded the Ballet Russe?

12. In *Amahl and the Night Visitors*, Amahl is a crippled shepherd boy. Who are the night visitors?

13. Which New Zealand soprano sang at the wedding of the Prince of Wales in 1981?

14. Who composed the music for *The Nutcracker*, *Sleeping Beauty* and *Serenade*?

15. The Royal Ballet, formerly known as the Sadler's Wells Ballet, was founded in 1931 by which dancer and choreographer?

16. The song 'Summertime' comes from which George Gershwin opera?

17. Which ballet tells the story of Franz, who falls in love with a mechanical doll, believing her to be a real woman?

18. Eight operas with the title *Turandot* have been written. Who wrote the most famous?

19. In 1987, what name did the Ballet Rambert take?

20. The opera *Rigoletto* is the story of the jester to the Duke of Mantua. What is Rigoletto's physical handicap?

21. Who is the choreographer of the ballets *Anastasia, Song of the Earth* and *Gloria*?

22. The author and broadcaster Ludovic Kennedy is married to which ballet dancer, star of the film *The Red Shoes*?

23. Three famous tenors sang in concert in 1990 and 1994. One tenor was Pavarotti. Who were the other two?

24. The 'Soldiers' Chorus' and 'Easter Fair Chorus' come from which Gounod opera?

25. Which Russian, born in 1890, became one of the world's most famous male dancers, but ended his carreer having succumbed to mental illness?

1. Canada has two official languages. What are they?

2. Which boat is made from a wickerwork frame covered with a leather skin?

3. Who plays con-man Harold Hill in the 1962 musical film *The Music Man*?

4. If the British call him a tramp, what would Americans call him?

5. GATT is an abbreviation for which agreement?

6. In heraldry, what colour is vert?

7. Lewis Carroll was an Oxford professor as well as a writer. What was his subject?

8. US comedian Jimmy Durante was known by what nickname?

9. What kind of creature is a Jonathan Livingston?

10. Snooker was invented in which country?

11. Elton John's 'Candle in the Wind' is a tribute to which star?

12. In which decade were tea bags first launched?

13. What was the previous name of Taiwan?

14. Which animal would you find living in a citadel?

15. Who is the hero of *The Thirty-Nine Steps*?

16. British rule in India was known by the Hindi word for 'sovereignty'. What is it?

17. In the rhyme 'Hickory Dickory Dock', what time did the clock strike?

18. Which elderly actress won an Oscar for best actress in *Driving Miss Daisy*?

19. Where would you find a monument popularly known as 'the wedding cake'?

20. What nationality was the artist Whistler?

21. One of the two families in the TV programme *Soap* was called Tate. What was the other family called?

22. Every Muslim aims to make a pilgrimage to Mecca once in a lifetime. Where is Mecca?

23. Which Latin term warns the buyer to beware when buying goods?

24. Animals that can live either on land or in water are called what?

25. Who said: 'An appeaser is one who feeds a crocodile, hoping it will eat him last'?

Geography and Travel • Conservation

1. Carbon dioxide
2. Power from water
3. India
4. The Persian Gulf
5. The shoots and leaves of bamboo
6. World Wide Fund for Nature
7. Chlorofluorocarbons (CFCs)
8. Global warming
9. Chernobyl
10. Tropical hardwood
11. The mountain regions of central Asia
12. Biomass power
13. Methane
14. Medicine
15. Ozone layer
16. Plutonium
17. Hunters considered them the 'right' whales to kill
18. Catalytic convertor
19. Green Party
20. They cannot be broken down by living organisms
21. Mountain gorillas
22. Uranium
23. Forest death
24. New World vulture
25. Three Mile Island

Popular Culture • Career Moves

1. Glenda Jackson
2. Swimming
3. John Glenn
4. Professor of religious philosophy
5. Kylie Minogue
6. Teaching
7. True
8. Aviation: she flew solo round the world
9. Danny Kaye
10. Newspaper journalist
11. Carmel
12. John Cleese
13. Engineer
14. Melina Mercouri
15. Apprentice hairdresser
16. Callan
17. Lauda Air
18. Policemen
19. Ronald Reagan
20. Whoopi Goldberg
21. Joan Rivers
22. Law
23. Teach engineering at the University of Cincinatti
24. Pilot on the Mississippi; it was one of the river cries
25. Michael Caine

Indoors and Out • Friends and Foes

1. Black rat
2. Cotton
3. Burrowing improves aeration and drainage of the soil
4. Dingo
5. China
6. Five
7. A mantle
8. Black fungus, sooty mould
9. Yes
10. Barn owl
11. In the tail
12. Dog
13. Weasel
14. It gnaws at the base, causing the tree to die
15. Females
16. Mole
17. Den
18. Cabbage White
19. Bluebottles and greenbottles
20. With an unpleasant-smelling discharge
21. Black Widow
22. Prairie dog
23. Glutton
24. It kills snakes
25. North America

Past and Present • The Irish Question

1. William Pitt
2. A fungus attacked the potato crop
3. Easter Rising
4. Phoenix Park
5. Irish Republican Army
6. Eire
7. Dáil Eireann or the Dáil
8. Sinn Fein
9. Peace Movement
10. Political parties
11. As a result of hunger strikes
12. Six
13. 1969
14. The Troubles
15. Black and Tans
16. 14 years
17. 'Birmingham Six'
18. Earl Mountbatten
19. Irish National Liberation Army
20. Kennedy
21. Harrods
22. It would not be changed without the consent of the majority of the people
23. Brighton
24. Gerry Adams
25. Democratic Unionist Party

Youth World • Developing Body

1. 20
2. 32
3. True
4. Ambidextrous
5. In the arm
6. 40%
7. Away from the heart
8. Antibodies
9. Testosterone
10. Men
11. 24
12. 70
13. Precocious puberty
14. Ball and socket
15. 18
16. Hydrochloric acid
17. The base of the neck
18. Metabolic rate
19. Plasma
20. Duodenum
21. Boys
22. Stirrup bone
23. Collar bone
24. 206
25. The outer layer of skin

Famous Folk • Fictional Characters

1. Ophelia
2. The East and West Witches
3. It is never revealed
4. Michael
5. Lois Lane
6. Peter Pan
7. Terry McCann
8. The fly
9. He has an enormous nose
10. David Copperfield
11. The Dormouse
12. Barbara and Oliver Rose
13. Dr Watson
14. Oliver Mellors
15. *The Enquirer*
16. Sally Bowles
17. They kept a shop
18. Earl of Huntingdon
19. Brown
20. Archaeologist
21. Passepartout
22. *Catcher in the Rye*
23. Purdey
24. Monckton
25. *Long Day's Journey Into Night*

Sport and Leisure • Opera and Ballet

1. Stravinsky
2. *Aida*
3. Australia
4. Metropolitan Opera House
5. *Swan Lake*
6. Contralto
7. William Tell
8. Terence Stamp
9. *Twilight of the Gods*
10. Five
11. Diaghilev
12. The three kings
13. Kiri Te Kanawa
14. Tchaikovsky
15. Ninette de Valois
16. *Porgy and Bess*
17. *Coppelia*
18. Puccini
19. Rambert Dance Company
20. He is a hunchback
21. Kenneth MacMillan
22. Moira Shearer
23. Carreras and Domingo
24. *Faust*
25. Nijinsky

Pot Luck

1. French and English
2. Coracle
3. Robert Preston
4. A hobo
5. General Agreement on Tariffs and Trade
6. Green
7. Mathematics
8. Schnozzle
9. Seagull
10. India
11. Marilyn Monroe
12. 1920s
13. Formosa
14. Mole
15. Richard Hannay
16. Raj
17. One
18. Jessica Tandy
19. Rome: the monument to Victor Emmanuel II
20. American
21. Campbell
22. Saudi Arabia
23. Caveat emptor
24. Amphibians
25. Winston Churchill

QUIZ

10

1. Which language is spoken by the descendants of Dutch and other immigrants who arrived in South Africa in the 17th century?

2. Name the race of hunter-gatherers of the African rainforests known for their small stature.

3. Where are the collective farms known as *kolkhoz*?

4. The Ainu are the aboriginal people of which country?

5. Approximately what percentage of the world's population is made up of Chinese?

6. Where does a Monegasque come from?

7. Name the nomadic people of northern Scandinavia.

8. The people of which country use zloty as currency?

9. Tok Pisin is now the official language of which country?

10. The Jains, who believe in complete non-violence, are a small religious community in which country?

11. Which people have often been called Eskimos, though they object to the name?

12. What are the indigenous Polynesian people of New Zealand called?

13. How did the Romany people get the name Gypsies?

14. What is the official language of Pakistan?

15. What is the official language of Iran?

16. In which part of South Africa would you be most likely to meet Zulus?

17. Where do women wear kimonos?

18. What is the language of the people of Haiti?

19. In which country are the Kikuyu the dominant ethnic group?

20. A murderous sect of Hindus that flourished in the 18th and 19th centuries specialized in violence against travellers. They have given their name to the language, describing a brutal and violent person. What is it?

21. What currency is used by people in Libya, Iraq and Jordan?

22. In which country would you meet Ibos?

23. Where do Walloons live?

24. What are the Paiute, Shoshone and Algonquin?

25. The Bedouin are desert nomads who scorn agricultural work. What is their occupation?

Q16

Q 14

1. In which continent did the poncho – a circular or rectangular piece of cloth with a hole for the head – originate?

2. What is a 'barbour', originally designed by John Barbour in 1890, but becoming popular for country wear this century?

3. Where would you wear gaiters?

4. Which hairdresser created the 'wash 'n' wear bob' in 1965?

5. In the 18th century, what was a banyan?

6. Which US designer created the influential 'prairie look', with denim skirts worn over layered white petticoats, in 1978?

7. What name is given to a divided skirt?

8. In which decade did the so-called 'peacock revolution' take place?

9. What were stays?

10. How did Americans come to use the name 'pants' to describe what the British call trousers?

11. Which designers were responsible for Lady Diana Spencer's wedding dress in 1981?

12. What were 'hot pants'?

13. What are espadrilles?

14. Which designer launched the 'New Look', with its small waist and full skirt, in the 1940s?

15. What was a fichu?

16. Which British designer closely associated with the punk movement launched the 'New Romantic' and the 'Pirate Look' in the late 1980s?

17. What shape was the mob cap of the 19th century?

18. The bustle, which made dresses stand out at the back, was eventually made from wire. What was it originally made from?

19. What is a dirndl skirt?

20. In which decade of the 19th century was the crinoline invented?

21. The 'A' line was created by Christian Dior in 1955. What shape was an 'A' line dress?

22. In the UK, 'Sloane Rangers' dress in timeless, classic clothes. What are their equivalent in the US called?

23. What was the chief feature of a poke hat?

24. What type of clothes are characteristic of the Gothic style, which became popular in the late 1980s?

25. The designer Giorgio Armani, who launched his own label in 1975, became famous for his suits and jackets. He is identified with which style for executive women?

1. Which plant takes its name from the Latin *lavare*, meaning to wash, because of its use in toilet preparations?

2. Which country do gladioli originally come from?

3. Which drug is derived from the poppy?

4. Which flower is sometimes called 'cut and come again' or 'youth and old age'?

5. Which flower is named after the Swiss botanist Charles Godet?

6. Give the collective name for the sepals of a flower.

7. Which perennial flowering herb with orange-yellow flowers is used in treatments for bruises and sprains?

8. What does 'dimorphoteca' mean in relation to a plant?

9. What colours will hydrangeas growing in acid soil normally be?

10. Which flowers can be floribunda or hybrid tea?

11. The flower called after the 16th-century German physician and herbalist Leonhart Fuchs is known as what?

12. How is the dahlia propagated?

13. What name is given to the male reproductive organ of a flower?

14. The flower sometimes known as bird of paradise was named after Queen Charlotte of Mecklenburg-Strelitz, wife of the English king George III. What is it?

15. Which flower has varieties including De Caen and St Brigid?

16. What is the popular name for *Impatiens*?

17. In which country is the growing and breeding of orchids centred?

18. The drug digitalis, a heart stimulant, comes from which flower?

19. Gaillard de Marentonneau, the French patron of botany, gave his name to which flower?

20. Which flowering tree has the botanical name *Prunus triloba*?

21. What name is given to the joint at which leaves are born on a stem?

22. What is the country of origin of lupins?

23. Which flower features in a song from *The Sound of Music*?

24. Give the popular name for antirrhinum.

25. Which type of begonia would be used as a show plant in containers, *Begonia semperflorens* or *Begonia tuberosa*?

1. Name the ex-prime minister of Italy who came under investigation after allegations of corruption.

2. Who was the American serial sex murderer killed by fellow inmates in prison in 1994?

3. Which boxer, sentenced to 10 years (four suspended) for rape in Indianapolis in 1992, was released in 1995?

4. George Michael lost his long-drawn-out battle with his recording company in 1994. Name the company.

5. In South Africa, much controversy has raged around Winnie Mandela. From which government post was she fired by her estranged husband?

6. How were businessmen Ernest Saunders, Gerald Ronson, Jack Lyons and Anthony Parnes linked in 1990?

7. Who married Michael Jackson soon after the scandal of alleged child abuse?

8. The film *Quiz Show*, directed by Robert Redford, concerns the scandal that rocked America in the 1950s. Name the quiz show involved.

9. Whose autobiography, entitled *My Lucky Stars: A Hollywood Memoir*, drew an unflattering portrait of Frank Sinatra and Dean Martin?

10. Qubilah Bahiyah Shabazz was charged with allegedly hiring a hitman to kill the leader of Nation of Islam. She is the daughter of which militant black leader?

11. Which British athlete, former Commonwealth 800 metres gold medalist, was banned for four years for alleged drug use?

12. When Spain celebrated its first royal wedding for 89 years, who was the bride?

13. Heart-throb tennis star Henri Leconte married Marie Sara. What is her claim to fame?

14. In a media context, what does 'outed' mean?

15. Camilla Parker-Bowles, friend of the Prince of Wales, announced her divorce in 1995. What is her husband's name?

16. What much-publicized confession did US talk show host Oprah Winfrey make on a programme about drugs?

17. Which top US comedy series star has accused her parents of abusing her as a child – accusations they strenuously deny?

18. John Wayne Bobbit hit the headlines when he was mutilated by his vengeful wife. What is her name?

19. A British advertising agency, known for publicizing the Conservative Party, was the scene of a boardroom battle, resulting in the resignation of the Chairman, though the firm bore his name. What was the firm?

20. Pamela Anderson of *Baywatch* is a favourite with the media. Name her pop-star husband.

21. Name the Hollywood 'madam' convicted of running a prostitution ring in a blaze of publicity.

22. French footballer Eric Cantona, playing for Manchester United, was disciplined after a violent episode at which ground?

Q23.

23. In 1994 Andrew Lloyd Webber replaced the lead in his latest musical when it opened on Broadway because 'she couldn't sing well enough.' She then sued him. Name the actress and the musical.

24. Which British actress, star of *Eastenders*, was in the headlines twice within a short space of time over incidents in cars?

25. O. J. Simpson's trial for murder monopolized the American media. What was his wife's name?

1. *Gunfight at the OK Corral* (1957) stars Burt Lancaster as Wyatt Earp. Who stars as Doc Holliday?

2. Give the title of the 1989 TV mini-series based on Larry McMurtry's Pulitzer Prize-winning novel.

3. Who plays the man with no name in *High Plains Drifter*?

4. Which comedy duo went *Way Out West* in 1937?

5. In *High Noon*, marshal Will Kane faces a gunman seeking revenge, against the wishes of his new Quaker bride. What is the film's theme song?

6. Who directs and stars in *Dances with Wolves*?

7. In the TV series *Maverick*, which of the Mavericks is played by James Garner?

8. What was Clark Gable's (and also Marilyn Monroe's) last film?

9. Yul Brynner, Steve McQueen, Brad Dexter, James Coburn and Horst Buchholz are five of *The Magnificent Seven*. Who are the other two?

10. 'Oh, What a Beautiful Morning' is the opening number of which western musical?

11. In the TV series, what aliases do Hannibal Heyes and 'Kid' Curry use?

12. Richard Harris plays an English aristocrat captured by which Indian tribe in *A Man Called Horse*?

13. The classic western *Stagecoach* made John Wayne a star. In which US setting was it filmed?

14. Which family lived on the Ponderosa ranch in *Bonanza*?

15. In *Unforgiven*, Clint Eastwood plays a retired gunfighter. How is he trying to earn a living?

16. Who directed the movies *Major Dundee* and *Junior Bonner* and the TV series *Gunsmoke* and *Have Gun, Will Travel*?

17. Three friends going through a mid-life crisis take a cattle drive vacation in *City Slickers*. Which veteran actor plays their ageing trail boss?

18. 'There's No Business Like Show Business' and 'Doin' What Comes Naturally' come from which musical?

19. Bob Hope stars in the comedy western *The Paleface* with which 1940s sex symbol?

20. In the long-running TV series *Wagon Train*, who plays the wagon-master?

21. *They Died with their Boots On* is the story of which flamboyant figure of the Old West?

22. Who directed the spoof western *Blazing Saddles*?

23. In *Seven Brides for Seven Brothers*, Howard Keel plays the eldest brother. Who plays the baby of the family?

24. Barbara Stanwyck stars as a wealthy ranch-owner in which 1960s TV series?

25. In which film does Spencer Tracy play a one-armed stranger arriving in a hostile town?

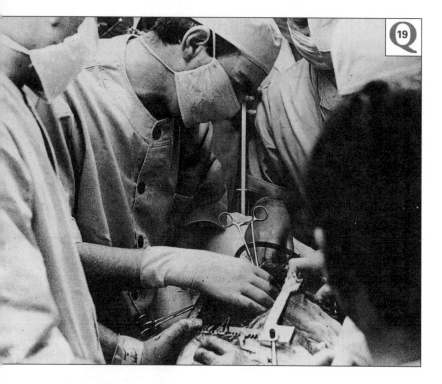

Q 19

5. Where was the British army hospital where that most famous of nurses Florence Nightingale worked to lamplight?

6. The ideas of Karl Marx had a dramatic effect and lasting effect on the politics and political ideologies of the 20th century. What was his most famous work?

7. Which prolific American inventor counted among his patents the printing telegraph, the microphone and gramophone?

8. Name the French philosopher who put forward his ideas, which were influential in the French Revolution, in the *Social Contract*?

1. In 1969 Neil Armstrong and Buzz Aldrin walked on the moon. Who stayed behind in the command module?

2. Who introduced the science of psychoanalysis, the investigation of the unconscious mind?

3. Which British philosopher and noted campaigner against nuclear weapons wrote the *History of Western Philosophy* and *Principia Mathematica*?

4. Alexander Graham Bell, inventor of the telephone, made the first long-distance call in 1892 from New York to which city?

9. Which missionary found the Victoria Falls in 1855 and set out to trace the source of the Nile, only to be 'lost' for a time in Africa?

10. Who set out his revolutionary ideas on the evolution of man in *The Origin of Species*?

11. What was the achievement of Bruce McCandless in space in 1984?

12. Andrei Sakharov campaigned for human rights in the USSR and was sentenced to internal exile in 1980. When was he released?

13. Name the three Pankhursts, mother and two daughters, who campaigned for votes for women in Britain in the 1880s.

14. What startling theory did Polish astronomer Copernicus put forward?

15. The first message sent in his special code in 1844 was 'What hath God wrought'. Who was he?

16. Frank Whittle was a pioneer in what field?

17. Name the Scot who invented a rainproof fabric, still used for raincoats.

18. Buffalo Bill's favourite weapon was the 'six-shooter'. Who had patented the revolver?

19. In which decade did Christiaan Barnard perform the first heart transplant?

20. The American Frederick Douglass was advisor to President Lincoln during the Civil War. Why was this remarkable?

21. What did Elisha Otis instal for the first time ever in a New York store in 1857?

22. Who invented a system to reduce background noise on audio equipment in 1967?

23. In what field did Friedrich Froebel pioneer?

24. Which new form of medicine did Samuel Hahnemann pioneer in the 19th century?

25. Mother Teresa is famous for her work among the poor in which city?

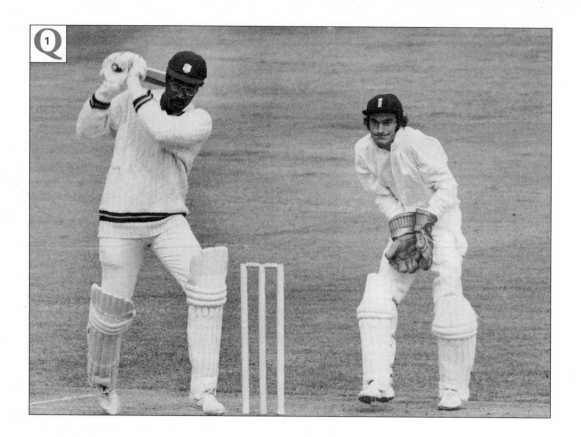

1. Which West Indian captain led his team in the most Test matches?

2. Who captained the first 'rebel' tour of South Africa?

3. How many players are there in an ice hockey team?

4. Who was the first man to win the Grand Slam in tennis?

5. In 1975 an Australia versus England cricket match had to be abandoned because of vandalism. Where was this?

6. How many innings would each side normally have during a game of baseball?

7. What are sandlotters?

8. In a game of fives, what do players use to hit the ball?

9. Which is the only tennis championship where women play the best of five sets?

10. Which batsman made the greatest number of centuries in his cricket career?

11. The first metal tennis racquets appeared in the 1920s. What were the strings made of?

12. At the beginning of an ice hockey match, the referee drops the puck on the ice between the sticks of opposing players. What is this procedure called?

13. Which Australian Test cricket player was nicknamed 'the unbowlable'?

14. In tennis, what score is called 'deuce'?

15. Who did Pete Sampras beat in the singles finals at Wimbledon in 1994?

16. In softball, how is the ball pitched?

17. The distances between bases are longer in softball than baseball. True or false?

18. If a cricket umpire raises both arms above his head, what is he signalling?

19. Which game was originally called 'sticky' by its detractors?

20. Who is the only West Indian cricketer to make a hundred hundreds?

Q14

21. What are the following: yorker, googly and chinaman?

22. In baseball, the fielding side is divided into three sections. What are they?

23. Rounders is usually played by women or children. How many innings does each team have?

24. If the server in tennis throws up a ball, attempts to hit it and misses, does it count as a fault?

25. Which baseball legend does Tommy Lee Jones play in a 1994 film?

Q 24

1. Which Victorian novelist created the fictional county of Barsetshire?

2. What do the French call the English channel?

3. 6 June 1944 is known as D-Day. What does the D stand for?

4. Name the largest island in the Caribbean.

5. Which composer did Dirk Bogarde play in *Song Without End*?

6. What would you be doing in a sulky?

7. In which TV series would you have heard about an organization called THRUSH?

8. Who painted a pile of Campbell's soup cans?

9. The film *Amadeus* was the story of which composer?

10. The following are models of which car: Riviera, Skylark and Skyhawk?

11. What is the currency of Iceland?

12. The Westchester Cup is awarded in which sport?

13. What modern convenience did Sir John Harrington design and instal for Queen Elizabeth I in her palace in Richmond, Surrey?

14. The works of which Italian painter include *St George and the Dragon*, now found in the Louvre, and *Coronation of the Virgin*, in the Vatican gallery?

15. In 1973 Cape Kennedy reverted to its former name. What is it?

16. Which gangster was nicknamed 'Baby Face'?

17. What type of animal is a cavicorn?

18. In medieval times, what would you be doing if you threw down the gauntlet?

19. Which country in Central America is known by the Spanish words for 'rich coast'?

20. In air travel, what does ETA stand for?

21. A famous novel is based on the real-life adventures of Alexander Selkirk. What is it called?

22. In which film did Bill Murray play a TV weatherman?

23. Gracie Fields sang about the 'cast-iron plant' by its other name. What is it?

24. What is boxer Barry McGuigan's nickname?

25. Which pop singer had hits with 'Delilah' and 'Green, Green Grass of Home'?

Geography and Travel • Peoples

1. Afrikaans
2. Pygmies
3. Russia
4. Japan
5. Over 25%
6. Monaco
7. Lapps
8. Poland
9. Papua New Guinea
10. India
11. Inuit
12. Maoris
13. They were wrongly

thought to come from Egypt
14. Urdu
15. Farsi
16. Natal
17. Japan
18. French
19. Kenya
20. Thug
21. Dinar
22. Nigeria
23. Belgium
24. They are all tribes of

Native Americans
25. Herding animals

Popular Culture • Fashion

1. South America
2. A waxed cotton jacket
3. Below the knee
4. Vidal Sassoon
5. A dressing gown
6. Ralph Lauren
7. Culottes
8. 1960s
9. Corsets stiffened with whalebone
10. Early trousers were similar to the leggings known as pantaloons

11. David and Elizabeth Emanuel
12. Very short shorts
13. Canvas shoes with braided cord soles
14. Christian Dior
15. A triangular shawl
16. Vivienne Westwood
17. A puffed crown with a deep frill
18. Horsehair
19. A full skirt gathered at the waist

20. 1850s
21. Narrow shoulders and wide hips
22. Preppies
23. A large brim
24. Black clothes, often with fringes and tears
25. The wide-shouldered look

Indoors and Out • Flowering Plants

1. Lavender
2. South Africa
3. Opium
4. Zinnia
5. Godetia
6. Calyx
7. Arnica
8. It produces two different kinds of seed
9. Blue and mauve
10. Roses
11. Fuchsia
12. By division of tubers

13. Stamen
14. Strelitzia
15. Anemone
16. Busy Lizzie
17. USA
18. Foxglove
19. Gaillardia
20. Flowering almond
21. Node
22. North America
23. Edelweiss
24. Snapdragon
25. *Begonia tuberosa*

Past and Present • Gossip, Gossip

1. Silvio Berlusconi
2. Jeffrey Dahmer
3. Mike Tyson
4. Sony
5. Deputy Minister of Arts, Culture, Science and Technology
6. They were the Guinness Four
7. Lisa Marie Presley
8. *Twenty-One*
9. Shirley MacLaine
10. Malcolm X

11. Diane Modahl
12. The Infanta Elena
13. She is the world's only female bullfighter
14. Homosexuals named without their consent
15. Andrew
16. She had used cocaine
17. Roseanne
18. Lorene
19. Saatchi and Saatchi
20. Tommy Lee
21. Heidi Fleiss

22. Crystal Palace
23. Faye Dunaway in *Sunset Boulevard*
24. Gillian Taylforth
25. Nicole

Youth World • Westerns

1. Kirk Douglas
2. *Lonesome Dove*
3. Clint Eastwood
4. Stan Laurel and Oliver Hardy
5. 'Do Not Forsake Me, Oh My Darlin''
6. Kevin Costner
7. Bret
8. *The Misfits*
9. Charles Bronson and Robert Vaughn
10. *Oklahoma*

11. Smith and Jones
12. Sioux
13. Monument Valley
14. The Cartwright family
15. Pig farming
16. Sam Peckinpah
17. Jack Palance
18. *Annie Get Your Gun*
19. Jane Russell
20. Ward Bond
21. George Armstrong Custer
22. Mel Brooks

23. Russ Tamblyn
24. *The Big Valley*
25. *Bad Day at Black Rock*

Famous Folk • Pioneers

1. Michael Collins
2. Sigmund Freud
3. Bertrand Russell
4. Chicago
5. The Crimea
6. *Das Kapital*
7. Thomas Edison
8. Jean-Jacques Rousseau
9. David Livingstone
10. Charles Darwin
11. The first untethered space walk
12. 1986

13. Emmeline, Sylvia and Christabel
14. That the earth moved round the sun
15. Samuel Morse
16. Jet propulsion
17. Charles Macintosh
18. Samuel Colt
19. 1960s
20. He was born a slave
21. A passenger elevator
22. Dolby
23. Kindergarten education

24. Homeopathy
25. Calcutta

Sport and Leisure • Bat and Ball

1. Clive Lloyd
2. Graham Gooch
3. Six
4. Fred Perry
5. Headingley
6. Nine
7. Amateur baseball players
8. The hand
9. Virginia Slims
10. Jack Hobbs
11. Piano wire
12. Face off

13. Bill Woodfull
14. Forty-all
15. Goran Ivanisevic
16. Underarm
17. False
18. A boundary six
19. Lawn tennis
20. Viv Richards
21. Styles of bowling
22. Battery, infield and outfield
23. Two
24. Yes

25. Ty Cobb

Pot Luck

1. Anthony Trollope
2. La Manche
3. Day
4. Cuba
5. Franz Liszt
6. Harness racing
7. *The Man from Uncle*
8. Andy Warhol
9. Mozart
10. Buick
11. Krona
12. Polo
13. A flush lavatory

14. Raphael
15. Cape Canaveral
16. George Nelson
17. One with hollow horns
18. Issuing a challenge to a duel
19. Costa Rica
20. Estimated time of arrival
21. *Robinson Crusoe*
22. *Groundhog Day*
23. Aspidistra
24. Clones Cyclone

25. Tom Jones

Q 4

1. In which Austrian town would you be able to visit Mozart's birthplace?

2. A bronze statue of Captain Bligh, of the *Bounty* mutiny fame, stands in Sydney, New South Wales. Why?

3. On which Christian site in Jerusalem does the Church of the Holy Sepulchre stand?

4. Name George Washington's home in Virginia, USA.

5. The Casa Guidi, where Elizabeth Barrett and Robert Browning lived after their elopement and marriage, now belongs to the Browning Institute. Which Italian city is it in?

6. Lizzie Borden's name became notorious when she was tried for the murder of her father and stepmother. The house in which the murders took place still stands in which Massachusetts town?

7. Which famous literary figure lived in the English town of Stratford-upon-Avon?

8. Name the novel that Victor Hugo wrote about the bellringer of a Paris cathedral.

9. Who attained enlightenment under a tree at Bodhgaya, in Bihar, India?

10. The Little Bighorn Battlefield National Monument, marking the scene of Custer's momentous defeat, is in which American state?

11. The writer often called 'Denmark's most famous son' was born in Odense, where his birthplace is now a museum. Who was he?

12. Which palace, now a top tourist attraction, was home to Henry VIII and is supposedly haunted by two of his wives?

13. Jesus gave a famous sermon on what is now known as the Mount of Beatitudes in the Jordan valley. The mount stands above which stretch of water?

14. Which New York square, at the heart of Greenwich Village, gave its name to the title of a novel by Henry James?

15. Name the Scottish poet who is remembered in museums at his birthplace in Alloway, Strathclyde and at the Tam O'Shanter Inn in Ayr.

16. Oscar Wilde's grave is in the Père Lachaise cemetery in Paris, where it was moved nine years after his death. Which famous sculptor produced the headstone?

17. Which Ernest Hemingway novel, set in the Spanish Civil War, was made into a film starring Ingrid Bergman?

18. In which German city can you visit Beethoven's birthplace and attend a concert in the Beethovenhalle?

19. The Captain Cook Memorial Museum is on New Zealand's Bay of Islands. In which ship did he sail round the country in 1769?

20. Laura Ingalls Wilder set the *Little House on the Prairie* books in Missouri but the original 'little house' and the farmhouse Charles Ingalls built in 1887 can be seen in which state?

21. Chartwell was Winston Churchill's home for 40 years. In which English county is Chartwell?

22. Which American state, where the restored home and law offices of Abraham Lincoln are situated, as well as the great man's tomb, is often called 'Land of Lincoln'?

23. The Napoleon museum is found in the Louis XV wing of the French palace in which he lived. Which palace is it?

24. Wild Bill Hickok and Calamity Jane are both buried above the town in South Dakota where Wild Bill was murdered. Name the town.

25. Which Jerusalem street, following the path taken by Jesus on his way to Golgotha, is now marked with the 'Stations of the Cross'?

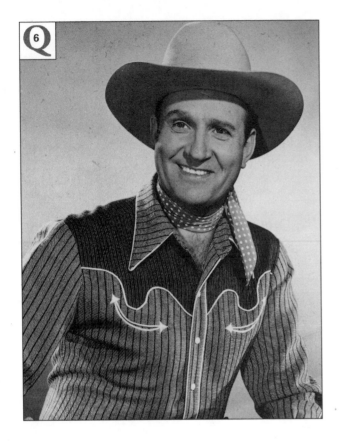

6. Gene Autry was the most successful of all singing cowboys to break into films. Name his horse.

7. Which country singer appeared in a US television series in the 1980s with her sisters Irlene and Louise?

8. Whose 1992 hit 'Achy Breaky Heart' led to a country music dance with the same name?

9. Which country star took her name from a hamburger stand?

10. The first female solo singer elected to the Country Music Hall of Fame in 1973 died in a plane crash in 1963. Who was she?

11. What is Stonewall Jackson's real name?

12. Name the vocalist who was born in England, grew up in Australia and was a country singer in the 1970s before going on to a more lucrative career in films like *Grease*.

1. Who recorded an album live in Folsom prison?

2. What are the first names of the Everly Brothers?

3. Which singer starred with John Wayne in *True Grit*?

4. Name Dolly Parton's Smoky Mountain theme park.

5. Who was known as the 'Singing Brakeman' and was later called the 'Father of Country Music'?

13. Who is the 'Coalminer's Daughter'?

14. Which star, known for his country music, wrote the all-time favourite 'Country Roads'?

15. Who made the award-winning double platinum album *Trio* with Linda Ronstadt and Dolly Parton?

16. Which country music legend was nicknamed the 'Drifting Cowboy'?

17. By what name is Virginia Wynette Pugh better known?

18. Which star, who began as Randy Traywick, then became Randy Ray before changing his name a second time, is said to be the 'first of the new traditionalists'?

19. Who wrote and performed 'Big Bad John' in the 1960s and later had hits with 'Stand Beside Me' and 'IOU'?

20. The 'International Ambassador of Country and Western Music' was the first American Western singer to perform in Russia and Czechoslavia. Who is he?

21. Which singer married Kris Kristofferson in 1973?

22. One of the richest men in country music, owner of a huge farm in Georgia, had one of his biggest hits with 'Islands in the Stream', a duet with Dolly Parton. Name him.

23. Which singer wrote 'Honeysuckle Rose' for the film of the same name and played Robert Redford's manager in *The Electric Horseman*?

24. In which town is the Grand Ole Opry?

25. Name the singer who starred with Jane Fonda and Lily Tomlin in the film *9 to 5*.

1. Which type of beans are used in Boston baked beans and in the French dish cassoulet?

2. The European types of sweet pepper are called paprikas. What do the Spanish call them?

3. Carrots are rich in which vitamin?

4. What vegetable is traditionally used in moussaka?

5. Tomatoes are now grown widely throughout the world, but where do they come from originally?

6. To which family does the globe artichoke belong?

7. What is Indian dhal made from?

8. By what name is the Lima or Madagascar bean often known?

9. Which type of garden peas are most used for canning and freezing?

10. In which country did the turnip originate?

11. Which name is given to the sun-dried peppers used to spice up Tabasco sauce and cayenne pepper?

12. Cabbage, kale and brussel sprouts are all members of which family?

13. Which vegetable is hollowed out and used as a lantern at Hallowe'en?

14. The chief pulse crop of India is called Bengal gram. By what name is it more commonly known?

15. There are two types of celery. One is the trenching variety. What is the other?

16. Potatoes are a crop of world-wide importance. Who were the first people in Europe to make great use of the potato in the early 17th century?

17. Chicory (endive) leaves are used in salads. Chicory is also dried, roasted and ground and mixed into which beverage?

18. Which vegetable would you find in Dubarry soup?

19. Beetroot is the main ingredient of which Russian soup?

20. What is the only cereal crop with American origins?

21. Which small type of cucumber is grown for pickling, where the immature fruits are soaked in brine and treated with boiling vinegar?

22. Kohlrabi is a cross between which vegetables?

23. Asparagus contains which vitamins?

24. What can be cherry, pear or potato-leaved?

25. Which vegetables are used in the famous New Orleans Creole dish gumbo?

Q 2

1. Which political group imposed dictatorship in France after the Revolution?

2. Who took over the reins of power in France after the Revolution?

3. In 1857, in the Indian Mutiny, sepoys serving under British officers refused to handle cartridges. Why?

4. In China, a young nationalist movement known as the 'Society of Harmonious Fists' rose against foreign influences in 1900. The rebellion was known by the society's nickname. What was it?

5. Lenin was the leading light of which revolutionary party in Russia?

6. Where were the Russian royal family shot in 1918?

7. The gladiator Spartacus led a slave revolt in Rome in 71BC. Who played Spartacus in the 1960 film of the same name?

8. A notorious massacre of 2000 Huguenots who had gathered in Paris in August, 1857, took place on which saint's day?

9. Which leader of the Cuban revolution took power in 1959?

10. In which year did the massacre of pro-democracy students in Tiananmen Square, Beijing, take place?

11. Which Italian ship was hijacked in the Mediterranean in October 1985?

12. What was the nationality of the gunman who shot Pope John Paul II in Rome in 1981?

13. Who led the liberal movement which was put down by the Russians in Czechoslovakia in 1968?

14. Riots in Los Angeles followed the acquittal of four white police officers on charges of beating up a black man in 1991. Who was he?

15. What revolution took place in Iran in 1979?

16. The Belgian Congo became independent in 1960 after nationalist riots. In 1971 it changed its name to what?

17. Pam Am Flight 103 was blown up over Lockerbie in 1988. In what had the bomb been planted?

18. Who was forced into exile from the Philippines in 1986?

19. Two million Armenians were massacred as a result of religious intolerance between 1895 and 1922. Which government was attempting to eliminate Armenia as a nation?

20. Which country revolted against the rule of the USSR in 1956?

21. In what year did General Franco become head of state in Spain after the Civil War?

22. In February 1993 a car bomb planted by Islamic Fundamentalists went off in the underground parking garage of which New York building?

23. In which capital city was there a suicide bomb attack on the US Embassy in 1976?

24. An airliner belonging to which country was hijacked and taken to Entebbe airport in 1976?

25. In which Jordan field were three airliners blown up by Arab guerillas in 1970?

Q 5

Q 8

3. In Aborigine legend, the world was formed in Dreamtime. In these stories, who provides the first light of dawn by lighting a fire to prepare a torch to carry through the day?

4. In the Grimm brothers' fairytale, why did the Sleeping Beauty fall asleep for 100 years?

5. What was the name of King Arthur's magic sword?

6. Who wrote an opera about Hansel and Gretel?

7. According to Irish mythology, what natural wonder was the beginning of a pathway built by the great warrior Finn McCool to link the coasts of Ireland and Scotland?

8. Pan was a mischievous, pipe-playing Greek god who was only half man. What was the other half?

9. In which mythology would you find Balder, Freyja and Loki?

10. How many labours did Hercules have to perform to atone for his crimes?

11. What did Cinderella leave behind when she fled from the ball?

12. The Greeks called him Eros. What did the Romans call him?

13. In ancient Canadian legend, what was the oldest and wisest creature on earth before man came to the Americas?

1. What was special about the relationship between Castor and Pollux?

2. Which epic poet wrote the *Iliad* and the *Odyssey*?

14. What did the Delphic oracle prophesy that Oedipus would do to his parents?

15. Thumbelina, a tiny girl not half as big as a thumb, was grown from a beggar's gift to a peasant woman who befriended her. What was it?

16. Which planet was named after the goddess of love?

17. Who was condemned to carry the world on his shoulders for making war on the gods?

18. Maui is the great hero of Maori legend. Which New Zealand island do the Maoris call Te Ika a Maui, meaning 'Maui's fishhook'?

19. What was the occupation of Snow White's seven dwarfs?

20. Medusa was one of the Gorgons. What did she have for hair?

21. Which Greek dramatist wrote *Oedipus Rex*, *Antigone* and *Electra*?

22. What high office did Dick Whittington eventually fill?

Q 17

23. In Greek mythology, which river did souls have to cross to get to Hades?

24. Whose wife was the Egyptian goddess Isis?

25. Who played Hans Christian Andersen in the 1952 film?

Q 4

5. How many children did John and Jackie Kennedy have?

6. Which brother did Ethel Skakel marry?

7. Which brother died when his plane exploded while on a World War II mission?

8. What political party did J. F. K. represent?

9. Which state did J. F. K. represent as senator?

10. What new feature appeared in the presidential campaign of 1960 when John F. Kennedy and Richard Nixon debated issues?

11. How old was J. F. K. when he was elected President?

12. What was the name of the young woman who died in 1969 when the car that Edward Kennedy was driving plunged off a bridge?

13. How did J. F. K.'s sister Kathleen die?

14. What was the international crisis during Kennedy's presidency that took the world close to nuclear war?

15. Which Kennedy sister was divorced from actor Peter Lawford?

16. In which year was J. F. K. assassinated?

17. Who shot Lee Harvey Oswald?

1. How many brothers and sisters did John F. Kennedy have?

2. Rose Kennedy, matriach of the family, died in January 1995. How old was she?

3. What was the first name of Rose's husband?

4. What was Jacqueline Kennedy's maiden name?

18. Who was sworn in as President immediately after the assassination?

19. Where is J. F. K. buried?

20. Which commission investigated the circumstances of the assassination?

21. Which brother married Joan Bennett?

23. John F. Kennedy was the first Catholic President of the US. True or false?

23. Who shot Robert Kennedy?

24. Where was Robert Kennedy assassinated?

25. John F. Kennedy Jnr has spent a year working on a new political publication called *George*, after George Washington. What was his previous job in Manhattan?

Q21

6. Which team has won eight team gold medals in Olympic Games dressage?

7. What age horses run in Triple Crown races in the US?

8. Name the jockey who overcame cancer to win the 1981 Grand National.

9. Ireland has produced some of the world's finest thoroughbred stock. Which racecourse is the home of all the Irish Classics?

10. The three-day event is still referred to as the *militaire* on the Continent because of its origins. Why?

11. Pierre Durand, France's Olympic gold medal winner in 1988, was still a part-time showjumper at the time, becoming full-time only in 1989. What was his previous profession?

1. What nationality is showjumping star Frankie Sloothaak?

2. In horse-jumping, what is the penalty for three refusals?

3. Where were the first World Equestrian Games held?

4. Name the horse that won the Derby by the greatest margin ever in 1981 and later disappeared.

5. How many players are there in a polo team?

12. In show-jumping, how many faults are incurred if horse and rider fall?

13. What relation are the showjumping riders Liz Edgar and David Broome?

14. How many fences in the Grand National are jumped twice?

15. What is the major race in Australia?

16. Which best-selling novelist wrote *Riders* and *Polo*?

17. Who was the first woman to win an individual gold medal in the Olympic Games in an equestrian event?

18. In horse-racing, what is a stayer?

19. The US race Arlington Million was first run in 1981 at Arlington Park, in which city?

20. Caroline Bradley, who died in 1983, was one of the world's best woman riders. She had a famous partnership with which horse?

21. Which showjumping rider holds most individual Olympic medals as individual rider and most titles as individual winner in World Championships?

22. In the film *National Velvet*, on which horse did Velvet Brown win the Grand National?

23. Where would riders encounter the Derby Bank?

24. The richest day's sport in the world is a US race meeting, held in October or November. What is it?

25. Puissance is a test of jumping ability. Where does the name come from?

Q 3

1. Who painted *The Night Watch*?

2. What would you make in a samovar?

3. Patrice Lumumba was the premier of which African country?

4. In which year was synchronized swimming first included in the Olympic Games?

5. Who said that a cauliflower is nothing but a 'cabbage with a college education'?

6. In the St Valentine's Day Massacre, members of Bugs Moran's gang were gunned down by members of which other gang?

7. Which character did Felicity Kendall play in TV's *The Good Life*?

8. Andrew Bonar Law was British Prime Minister from 1922 to 1923. In which country was he born?

9. Who was assassinated by Nathuran Godse in 1948?

10. What is an animal's pug?

11. Which country is divided into 23 cantons?

12. In what type of painting did the artist Giovanni Bellini specialize?

13. Who would eat Halal meat?

14. In many countries, some insects are regarded as delicacies. Which insects are the most popular snacks?

15. What is unusual about the Chinese Crested dog?

16. Which father and daughter topped the charts with 'Something Stupid' in 1967?

17. Name Shirley MacLaine's actor brother.

18. In which country was Laurens van der Post born?

19. King George V changed the name of the British royal family to Windsor. What had it been previously?

20. The Parthenon in Athens belongs to which order of architecture?

21. Who was Liza Minelli's famous mother?

22. What animal married the Owl and Pussycat after they had gone to sea together?

23. *Sophie's Choice*, a novel by William Styron, was filmed in 1982. Who played Sophie?

24. Amy is a girl's name that comes from Old French. What does it mean?

25. The 'Star-Spangled Banner' became the US national anthem by Act of Congress in 1931. Who wrote the words?

Q19

Answers to Quiz 11

Geography and Travel • In the Footsteps

1. Salzburg
2. He was governor of New South Wales
3. The site of the crucifixion
4. Mount Vernon
5. Florence
6. Fall River
7. Shakespeare
8. *The Hunchback of Notre Dame*
9. Buddha
10. Montana
11. Hans Christian Andersen
12. Hampton Court
13. Sea of Galilee
14. Washington Square
15. Robert Burns
16. Jacob Epstein
17. *For Whom the Bell Tolls*
18. Bonn
19. *Endeavour*
20. South Dakota
21. Kent
22. Illinois
23. Fontainebleau
24. Deadwood
25. Via Dolorosa

Popular Culture • Country and Western

1. Johnny Cash
2. Don and Phil
3. Glen Campbell
4. Dollywood
5. Jimmy Rodgers
6. Champion
7. Barbara Mandrell
8. Billy Ray Cyrus
9. Crystal Gayle
10. Patsy Cline
11. Stonewall Jackson
12. Olivia Newton-John
13. Loretta Lynn
14. John Denver
15. Emmylou Harris
16. Hank Williams
17. Tammy Wynette
18. Randy Travis
19. Jimmy Dean
20. George Hamilton IV
21. Rita Coolidge
22. Kennie Rogers
23. Willie Nelson
24. Nashville, Tennessee
25. Dolly Parton

Indoors and Out • Vegetable Crop

1. Haricot beans
2. Pimiento
3. Vitamin A
4. Aubergine (eggplant)
5. South America
6. The daisy family
7. Lentils
8. Butter bean
9. Marrowfat
10. Greece
11. Chillies
12. Brassica
13. Pumpkin
14. Chickpea
15. Self-blanching
16. The Irish
17. Coffee
18. Cauliflower
19. Bortsch
20. Corn
21. Gherkins
22. Cabbage and turnip
23. B and C
24. Tomato
25. Okra, green peppers, celery and onions

Past and Present • Revolution and Riots

1. Jacobins
2. Maximilian Robespierre
3. They believed they were coated with cow and pig grease
4. Boxer Rebellion
5. Bolsheviks
6. Ekaterinburg
7. Kirk Douglas
8. St Bartholomew's Day
9. Castro
10. 1989
11. *Achille Lauro*
12. Turkish
13. Alexander Dubcek
14. Rodney King
15. Islamic revolution
16. Zaire
17. In a radio/tape recorder
18. Ferdinand and Imelda Marcos
19. Turkish government
20. Hungary
21. 1939
22. World Trade Center
23. Beirut
24. France
25. Dawson's Field

Youth world • Myth and Fairytale

1. They were identical twin brothers
2. Homer
3. The Sun Woman
4. She pricked her finger on a spindle
5. Excalibur
6. Humperdinck
7. The Giant's Causeway
8. Goat
9. Norse
10. 12
11. A glass slipper
12. Cupid
13. The turtle
14. Kill his father and marry his mother
15. A barleycorn
16. Venus
17. Atlas
18. North Island
19. Diamond miners
20. Serpents
21. Sophocles
22. Lord Mayor of London
23. Styx
24. The wife of Osiris
25. Danny Kaye

Famous folk • The Kennedys

1. Eight
2. 104
3. Joseph
4. Bouvier
5. Three; one died in infancy
6. Robert
7. Joseph
8. Democrat
9. Massachusetts
10. The first-ever live TV presidential debate
11. 43
12. Mary Jo Kopechne
13. In a plane crash
14. Cuban missile crisis
15. Patricia
16. 1963
17. Jack Ruby
18. Lyndon B. Johnson
19. Arlington National Cemetery
20. Warren Commission
21. Edward
22. True
23. Sirhan B. Sirhan
24. Ambassador Hotel, Los Angeles
25. Assistant district attorney

Sport and Leisure • Horsy Sports

1. Dutch
2. Elimination
3. Stockholm
4. Shergar
5. Four
6. Germany
7. Three-year-olds
8. Bob Champion
9. The Curragh
10. It originated as a test for officers' chargers
11. Lawyer
12. Eight
13. Brother and sister
14. 14
15. Melbourne Cup
16. Jilly Cooper
17. Marian Mould
18. A horse that can gallop at racing pace over 2.4 km (1½ miles) or further
19. Chicago
20. Milton
21. Hans Günter Winkler
22. The Pie
23. Hickstead, Sussex
24. Breeders' Cup Day
25. It is French for 'power'

Pot Luck

1. Rembrandt
2. Tea
3. The Congo
4. 1984
5. Mark Twain
6. Al Capone's
7. Barbara Good
8. Canada
9. Gandhi
10. Footprint
11. Switzerland
12. Devotional pictures of the Madonna
13. Muslims
14. Grasshoppers
15. It is hairless
16. Nancy and Frank Sinatra
17. Warren Beatty
18. South Africa
19. Saxe-Coburg-Gotha
20. Doric
21. Judy Garland
22. Turkey
23. Meryl Streep
24. Loved
25. Francis Scott Key

1. What is the longest river in India?

2. China was the birthplace of two religions. One is Taoism, what is the other?

3. The tsetse fly, found in Africa, spreads what disease?

4. Which country, the most populated in Africa, is often called 'the Giant of Africa'?

5. What is a calabash?

6. Which country is the largest producer of tungsten?

7. The world's highest active volcano is in Ecuador. What is it called?

8. In which country is the ancient town of Timbuktu?

9. What is the largest and most sparsely populated state in Central America?

10. Rwanda obtained its independence from which country in 1962?

11. Why are the Blue Mountains of Jamaica so called?

12. When does the wet season begin in India?

13. What is puja?

14. The OAU was set up in 1963 at the conference of Addis Ababa, its aim to promote unity among African states. What do the initials stand for?

15. Varanasi is one of the most sacred of Hindu cities. Pilgrims bathe from the 'ghats', or stairs, in which river?

16. What is Columbia's largest export?

17. Name the capital and chief port of Nigeria.

18. The Ruwenzori mountains are found on the border between which countries?

19. The highest mountain in the world is found in the Himalayas. What does 'Himalayas' mean?

20. The most devastating floods in Bangladesh were in 1970, before the country gained independence. What was it called at that time?

21. The Live Aid concert was organized to raise money for the famine victims of which country?

22. Which fertile state in India is often called the 'granary of India'?

23. What name is given to the ruler of a Muslim state?

24. The Masai Mara game park in Kenya is on the Serengeti Plain. What is the dramatic setting of the second most popular Kenyan game park, Amboseli?

25. Which mountain range is known as the 'roof of the world'?

Q22

5. Which poet invited Maud to come into the garden?

6. Barbara Cartland, one of the world's most prolific novelists, extols the virtue of vitamin supplements and what natural food?

7. In *Gone with the Wind*, Rhett Butler loves Scarlett O'Hara. Who does Scarlett love?

8. Clark Gable and Carole Lombard were both movie idols when they met, eloped and married in secret. How did she die in 1942?

9. Which character sings 'If Ever I Would Leave You' in *Camelot*?

10. In Shakespeare's *Romeo and Juliet*, Romeo belongs to the Montagu family. Which family does Juliet belong to?

11. Why does Miss Havisham, in *Great Expectations*, live as a recluse in a white dress and veil?

12. Which couple married in Canada in 1964 and again in 1975 in Botswana?

13. 'Stranger in Paradise' and 'This is my Beloved' are songs from which musical?

14. Which classic screen love story begins with Alec removing a cinder from Laura's eye on a railway station and progresses to a score by Rachmaninov?

15. Who is Hiawatha's beloved in the poem of that name by Longfellow?

1. The love story of which writer is portrayed in *Shadowlands*?

2. The songs 'If I Loved You' and 'You'll Never Walk Alone' come from which musical?

3. In which country did the Duke of Windsor and his wife take up residence after his abdication?

4. Who married his *Days of Thunder* co-star?

16. During the making of which film did Humphrey Bogart and Lauren Bacall meet and fall in love?

17. Who plays the insomniac widower in *Sleepless in Seattle*?

18. Which poet's love is like 'a red, red rose that's newly sprung in June'?

19. In *Dr Zhivago*, who has a passionate affair with the hero?

20. Which character washes a man right out of her hair in *South Pacific*?

21. Who plays the two characters who plan a sexy vacation in Spain and then fall in love by mistake in *A Touch of Class*?

22. In which novel by Charlotte Brontë does a governess marry the master of Thornfield Hall?

23. Where do two ex-lovers meet under dramatic circumstances in *Casablanca*?

24. In which Jane Austen novel does Elizabeth Bennet fall in love with Mr Darcy?

25. When is St Valentine's Day?

1. What name is given to the dragonfly larva that hatches from the egg?

2. Where does the mandarin duck nest?

3. How would you distinguish an alligator from a crocodile, at a glance?

4. The papyrus plant, once plentiful in the Nile Delta, is now an endangered plant in Egypt. What was papyrus used for in ancient Egypt?

5. Daphnia and cyclops are types of which creature?

6. What are the smallest type of plants found in a pond called?

7. The pondskater uses its hind legs as rudders and its middle legs as oars. What are the front legs for?

8. What do the plants Canadian pondweed, bladderworts, milfoil and hornwort have in common?

9. Dippers are found in Europe, the Americas, West Africa and Asia, feeding on snails, tadpoles and larvae. How do they find their food?

10. How does the male stickleback fish attract a mate?

11. What is the largest and heaviest water-bird of freshwater lakes and rivers?

12. The Australian platypus is a monotreme. What is a monotreme?

13. When do some drakes go into 'eclipse' plumage?

14. Which flowers had the reputation as a symbol of immortality in ancient times?

15. What is the otter's home called?

16. The plants with poker-shaped heads that usually feature in pictures of Moses in the bulrushes, are not true bulrushes. What are they?

17. What name is given to young fish, especially salmon and trout?

18. Female frogs lay their eggs in water. What do they hatch into?

19. The water spider spends its whole life under water. How does it create a place to mate and lay its eggs?

20. What is a beaver's home called?

21. The medicinal leech produces a chemical which can have a use in medical practice. What does it do?

22. For its first three years in the river, a salmon is known as a 'parr'. When it migrates to the sea it is known as what?

23. The heaviest snake is the water boa of northern South America. What is it usually called?

24. Water lettuce is a floating plant with rosette leaves which is often used to coat the surface of tropical ponds and fish tanks as it keeps the water cool and fresh. What is its disadvantage?

25. The Jaçana bird has long, widespread toes that enable it to walk across leaves in its search for insects and seeds. What is its nickname?

213

1. In which decade of the 19th century was the Ku Klux Klan originally founded?

2. What do the initials WASP stand for?

3. What was the meaning of 'apartheid'?

4. What was the Holocaust?

5. In 1937 Hitler told a sitting of the Reichstag that Germans needed *Lebensraum*. What did this mean?

6. Which Jews were first boycotted under Hitler's anti-Semitic decrees?

7. Who took control of the ruthless SS from 1929?

8. Chelmno was the first example of an important instrument of Hitler's plans. What was it?

9. Josef Goebbels was Hitler's right-hand man. How did he die?

10. Adolf Eichmann, who was personally responsible for the operation of extermination centres, escaped after the war. Where was he eventually kidnapped by Israeli agents?

11. Where was the largest Jewish ghetto, the scene of an uprising in 1943?

12. The battle of Wounded Knee in 1890 involved which minority ethnic group?

13. In America, what do the initials CORE stand for?

14. What did the 'Jim Crow' laws, enacted in various American states, seek to do?

15. 'The Little Rock Nine' were black students who took their places in a previously segregated High School against strenuous local opposition. In which American state is Little Rock?

16. In 1955 Rosa Parks refused to give up her seat to a white man in a bus in Alabama and was imprisoned as an agitator. What incident followed?

17. In the early 1960s, South African police enforced security laws run by BOSS. What do the initials stand for?

18. What are the 'Bantustans'?

19. Which South African 'black consciousness' leader died from severe brain damage while in police custody in 1977?

20. What is Soweto short for?

21. Which notorious massacre took place at a South African township in 1960, when police opened fire on a crowd demonstrating against the pass laws?

22. In which year was Nelson Mandela sentenced to life imprisonment?

23. Who took over from Mandela as ANC leader?

24. What church did civil rights leader Martin Luther King belong to?

25. In the 1970s the Rhodesian government found itself fighting with ZAPU and ZANU. ZAPU was the Zimbabwe Africa People's Union. What was ZANU?

1. Who starred as Helen Keller at the age of 16 and as Helen's teacher in a TV version of the same work 17 years later?

2. Which father and daughter star in *Tiger Bay*?

3. In which film does Lukas Hass play a young Amish boy who sees a murder ?

4. Scott Baio plays the title character in *Bugsy Malone*. Who plays Tallulah?

5. How old was Judy Garland when she appeared in *The Wizard of Oz*?

6. In which film do three children, played by Hayley Mills, Alan Barnes and Diane Holgate, find a killer they believe to be Jesus Christ?

7. Which teenage singer-actor of the 1930s went on to star with Gene Kelly in *Singin' in the Rain*?

8. Eight-year-old Margaret O'Brien stars in *Our Vines Have Tender Grapes*. Who plays her Wisconsin farmer father?

9. Ricky Schroder made his debut at age nine in a film about prize-fighting, with Jon Voigt and Faye Dunaway as his parents. Name the film.

10. How old was Tatum O'Neal when she won the Best Supporting Actress award for *Paper Moon*?

11. In which film do youngsters Jon Whiteley and Vincent Winter find a baby on a Scottish hillside and decide to keep it as a pet?

12. *Home Alone* made Macaulay Culkin a star. Name the 1995 film in which he plays a youngster who becomes a millionaire after his parents are killed in a plane crash.

13. Bette Davis plays a former child star grown old and embittered in which film?

14. Deanna Durbin was a teenage singer-actress who launched her film career along with Judy Garland in a short film called *Every Sunday* in 1936. What is her nationality ?

15. What role does young Henry Thomas play in *ET*?

16. Which member of a well-known acting family plays one of the Banks family in *Mary Poppins*?

17. The 1947 version of *Miracle on 34th Street* stars a child actress who later went on to star as Gypsy Rose Lee. Who is she?

18. In a classic western Brandon de Wilde plays Joey, idolizing a former gunfighter who comes to the rescue of homesteaders menaced by an all-powerful cattle baron. Name the film.

19. Which child star of the 1970s made her debut as a director with *Little Man Tate*, about the problems of a child genius?

20. Which child actress is the eldest of *The Railway Children*?

21. Tatum O'Neal appeared in *Bad News Bears* which revolved around which sport?

22. Which former child actress became US ambassador to Czechoslovakia in the late 1980s?

23. Linda Blair gives an electrifying performance as the girl possessed by demons in *The Exorcist*. Who wrote the book on which the film is based?

24. Mark Lester plays the title role in *Oliver!* Who plays the Artful Dodger?

25. As a child, Roddy McDowall tugged at the heartstrings in *How Green Was My Valley*. In the 1960s he appeared in a science fiction film which was to inspire several sequels as well as animated cartoons and a TV series. Name it.

Q 25

1. Who was the first king of Israel?

2. In which country has Queen Margrethe II reigned since 1972?

3. Which German ruler did Queen Victoria's eldest daughter marry in 1858?

4. Who is the only son of Prince Rainier of Monaco?

5. Which royal house ruled Austria from the 15th century to 1918?

6. For how long did Lady Jane Grey reign in England in 1553?

7. Juan Carlos was restored to the Spanish throne after Franco's death. He married a princess from which country?

8. Who plays King Faisal in the 1962 film *Lawrence of Arabia*?

9. Which Roman general became Cleopatra's lover and ruled Egypt with her?

10. Brian Boru became king of which country in 1001?

11. Who was the legendary first king of Rome, ruling for 40 years?

12. Madame du Barry was the influential mistress of which French king?

13. The rulers of the Netherlands, currently represented by Queen Beatrix, belong to which royal house?

14. Where was Princess Elizabeth when she heard that her father had died and she was Queen of Britain?

15. Which Babylonian king conquered the kingdom of Judah and sacked Jerusalem, sending the Hebrews into captivity in Babylon?

16. Which king of Prussia was chosen as the first emperor of Germany in 1871?

17. What Australian city was named after the wife of William IV of Britain?

18. In which kingdom did the house of Wittelsbach reign?

19. Which French king re-established the Bourbon dynasty after the downfall of Napoleon, reigning from 1815 to 1824?

20. At what age did Queen Victoria come to the throne?

21. Peter II was the last king of Yugoslavia. After his exile in 1945, who came to power in the country?

22. In which country were Simeon, Boris, Ferdinand and Ivan Shishman kings?

23. Who was technically the last Tsar of Russia, becoming Emperor in 1721?

24. In the film *The Madness of King George*, who plays Queen Charlotte?

25. Which of Henry VIII's wives outlived him?

1. After how many penalty points is a contestant in a wrestling bout eliminated?

2. What used to be called a battledore?

3. When did Torvill and Dean first win the World Ice Dancing Championship?

4. Which immigrants introduced nine-pin bowling to the US?

5. On how many pieces of apparatus do men compete in international gymnastic competition?

6. On how many pieces of apparatus do women gymnasts compete?

7. At the beginning of a basketball game, the referee throws up the ball in the centre circle. What is this called?

8. A table tennis game is won by the first player to reach how many points?

9. Ice hockey has its historical roots in which country?

10. A game of pool is made up of an agreed number of 'sections', each played to an agreed point requirement. What are these sections called?

11. What is special about a three cushion billiard table?

12. Which is the most successful country in Olympic boxing?

13. Whose set of rules was adopted in boxing in 1865?

14. What is the nickname of basketball player Irvine Johnson?

15. In November 1994 who regained the world heavyweight boxing title he lost 20 years earlier to Muhammad Ali ?

16. In which sport is the Uber Cup awarded?

17. What is the lowest possible score to conclude a game of darts?

18. In which sport might you see an Endocircle, Elgrip swing or Voronin hop?

19. When is a spare scored in ten-pin bowling?

20. In 1985 Steve Davis came close to winning his third successive world title with a lead of 8–0 but his opponent came from behind to beat him. Who was he?

21. Basketball has five players a side. How many does netball have?

22. In an American game of squash, both server and receiver can score. True or false?

23. How many balls are used in a game of pool?

24. Badminton became an Olympic sport quite recently. Give the year.

25. Which British boxer had a left hook, with which he once floored Muhammad Ali, known as 'Enery's 'ammer'?

1. In dice, what are 'snake eyes'?

2. Who caught the German war-criminal Adolf Eichmann after World War II?

3. Which famous group was led by Guy Gibson in World War II?

4. In heraldry, what is a creature in a lying position called?

5. Which actress stars in *Anatomy of a Murder* and *Days of Wine and Roses*?

6. Halley's Comet, named after Edmond Halley who calculated its orbit, will next reappear in which year?

7. Name the singer who had hits with 'Pretty Woman' and 'Only the Lonely'.

8. Which school of architecture was associated with Walter Gropius?

9. What is the middle name of the Princess of Wales?

10. Name the sauce made from mayonnaise, chopped capers and onions and served with fish?

11. What was the first Rolls Royce model called?

12. Which is the largest of the Canadian provinces?

13. In which sea are the group of islands called Tristan da Cunha?

14. In 1991 *Dances with Wolves* won an Oscar for best picture. Who won the best director award for the same film?

15. What name is given to a male swan?

16. What is the unit of weight used to measure gemstones?

17. In which musical does a Scottish village become visible for only one day in every hundred years?

18. What is a group of porpoises called?

19. Who wrote *The Birthday Party* and *The Caretaker*?

20. Which film star said: 'You are not drunk if you can lie on the floor without holding on'?

21. On which part of the body would you wear puttees?

22. Which city was often painted by Canaletto?

23. What is the capital of Burma?

24. Rachel, a name that appears in the Old Testament, comes from the Hebrew. What does it mean?

25. What do the novelist J. R. R. Tolkien's initials stand for?

Geography and Travel • Third World

1. Brahmaputra
2. Confucianism
3. Sleeping sickness
4. Nigeria
5. A gourd, hollowed out to hold liquids
6. China
7. Cotopaxi
8. Mali
9. Nicaragua
10. Belgium
11. There is a bluish haze over them
12. June
13. A form of religious worship for Hindus
14. Organization of African Unity
15. Ganges
16. Cocaine
17. Lagos
18. Uganda and Zaire
19. Abode of snow
20. East Pakistan
21. Ethiopia
22. Punjab
23. Emir
24. Below Mount Kilimanjaro
25. Karakoram

Popular Culture • Romance

1. C.S. Lewis
2. *Carousel*
3. France
4. Tom Cruise
5. Tennyson
6. Honey
7. Ashley Wilkes
8. In a plane crash
9. King Arthur
10. Capulet
11. She was jilted on her wedding day
12. Elizabeth Taylor and Richard Burton
13. *Kismet*
14. *Brief Encounter*
15. Minnehaha
16. *To Have and Have Not*
17. Tom Hanks
18. Robert Burns
19. Lara
20. Nellie Forbush
21. Glenda Jackson and George Segal
22. *Jane Eyre*
23. Rick's bar
24. *Pride and Prejudice*
25. 14 February

Indoors and Out • Pond and River Life

1. Nymph
2. In a hole in a tree
3. The alligator's teeth do not project when the jaw is closed
4. Paper and sails
5. Water-fleas
6. Algae
7. Grabbing insects for food
8. They all float on the water surface
9. They dive into the water and walk along the bottom
10. He dances for her
11. Mute swan
12. An egg-laying mammal
13. Outside the breeding season
14. Waterlilies
15. Holt
16. Reed mace
17. Alevin
18. Tadpoles
19. It spins a web between plants that acts as a diving bell
20. Lodge
21. It prevents blood clotting
22. Smolt
23. Anaconda
24. It spreads quickly
25. Lily-trotter

Past and Present • Race Relations

1. 1860s
2. White Anglo-Saxon Protestant
3. Separate development
4. Persecution and destruction of Jews by the Nazis
5. Living space
6. Shopkeepers, doctors and lawyers
7. Heinrich Himmler
8. Extermination camp
9. He shot himself
10. Argentina
11. Warsaw
12. Native Americans
13. Congress of Racial Equality
14. Limit the rights of blacks
15. Arkansas
16. A boycott of buses by the blacks
17. Bureau of Social Security
18. South African homelands
19. Steve Biko
20. South-West Township
21. Sharpeville massacre
22. 1964
23. Oliver Tambo
24. Baptist
25. Zimbabwe African National Union

Youth World • Young Stars

1. Patty Duke
2. John and Hayley Mills
3. *Witness*
4. Jodie Foster
5. Seventeen
6. *Whistle Down the Wind*
7. Donald O'Connor
8. Edward G. Robinson
9. *The Champ*
10. 10
11. *The Kidnappers*
12. *Richie Rich*
13. *Whatever Happened to Baby Jane?*
14. Canadian
15. Elliott
16. Karen Dotrice
17. Natalie Wood
18. *Shane*
19. Jodie Foster
20. Jenny Agutter
21. Little League baseball
22. Shirley Temple Black
23. Peter Blatty
24. Jack Wild
25. *Planet of the Apes*

Famous Folk • International Royalty

1. Saul
2. Denmark
3. Frederick III
4. Prince Albert
5. Hapsburg
6. Nine days
7. Greece
8. Alec Guinness
9. Mark Antony
10. Ireland
11. Romulus
12. Louis XV
13. Orange
14. Kenya
15. Nebuchadnezzar
16. William I
17. Adelaide
18. Bavaria
19. Louis XVIII
20. 18
21. Tito
22. Bulgaria
23. Peter the Great
24. Helen Mirren
25. Catherine Parr

Sport and Leisure • Indoor Sports

1. Six
2. Badminton racquet
3. 1981
4. Dutch and German
5. Five
6. Three
7. Jump ball
8. 21
9. Canada
10. Blocks
11. It has no pockets
12. USA
13. Marquess of Queensberry
14. Magic
15. George Forman
16. Badminton
17. Two
18. Men's gymnastics
19. When a player knocks down all 10 pins with both balls in a frame
20. Dennis Taylor
21. Seven a side
22. True
23. One white ball and 15 numbered object balls
24. 1992
25. Henry Cooper

Pot Luck

1. Two
2. Dr. Simon Wiesenthal
3. The Dambusters
4. Couchant
5. Lee Remick
6. 2061
7. Roy Orbison
8. Bauhaus
9. Frances
10. Tartare sauce
11. Silver Ghost
12. Quebec
13. Atlantic
14. Kevin Costner
15. Cob
16. Carat
17. *Brigadoon*
18. A school
19. Harold Pinter
20. Dean Martin
21. On the legs
22. Venice
23. Rangoon
24. Ewe
25. John Ronald Reuel

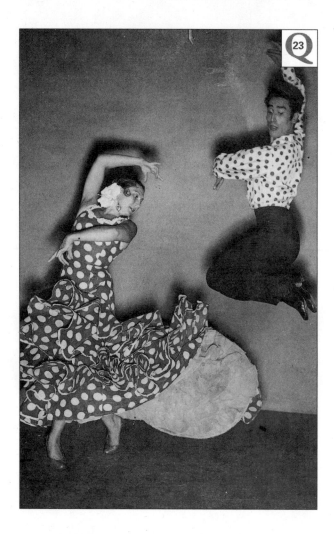

23 Q

3. What would you find in the Prado, Madrid?

4. Name the Scottish royal residence bought by Queen Victoria and Prince Albert as a summer home in 1848.

5. What does the Bayeux tapestry record?

6. Where is the headquarters of the World Health Organization?

7. What is the smallest state in the world?

8. Which European city consists of 118 islands linked by 400 bridges?

9. In which German town is a passion play performed every 10 years?

10. The leaning Tower of Pisa is a popular tourist attraction. What is it?

11. In which part of Paris is the Cathedral of Notre Dame?

12. Monte Marmolada is the highest peak in which mountain range?

13. In which country would you find the ports of Cartagena, Santander and Bilbao?

14. In the old song, which Irish mountains 'sweep down to the sea'?

1. Which town gives its name to the French national anthem because so many of its revolutionaries marched on Paris in 1792?

2. Where is the oldest oracle in Greece, dedicated to Zeus?

15. Which country is sometimes called the 'Hexagon' because it is roughly six-sided?

16. In which mountain range would you find the ski resort of St Moritz?

17. What do the frescoes on the ceiling of the Sistine Chapel in Rome, painted by Michelangelo, depict?

18. In which Italian town is a horse race called the Palio run around the main piazza?

19. What is the oldest part of the Tower of London, built for William the Conqueror?

20. Name the flat, marshy area of south-east France, famous as a breeding ground for bulls and horses.

21. On which French bridge, according to the song, did everyone dance in a ring?

22. In which city would you find the statue of the Little Mermaid?

23. In which country would you find flamenco dancers?

24. What is the highest peak in the Alps?

25. Which wall was built across the north of England to defend the northern frontier of the Roman empire?

1. Which British actress played Sable Colby in *Dynasty*?

2. Name the former star of *Neighbours* who had a 1990 hit with 'Another Night'.

3. Both *Brookside* and *Emmerdale Farm* have introduced lesbian characters. Who are they?

4. In *Eastenders*, who was sent to prison after a drink-drive accident?

5. *Home and Away* takes place in which seaside resort?

6. Name the three founder members of Ewing Oil in *Dallas*.

7. In *Falcon Crest*, what was Angela Channing's maiden name?

8. Which brewery owns the Rover's Return in *Coronation Street*?

9. The Colbys was a short-lived spin-off of *Dynasty*. Who appeared in the series as the glamorous Maya Kumara?

10. In *Neighbours*, who ran over Cheryl Stark after an argument?

11. What is the name of the restaurant set up by Barry and Max in *Brookside*?

12. In *Knots Landing*, who is Gary and Val's eldest daughter, a central character in early episodes of Dallas?

13. In *Dynasty*, Pamela Sue Martin first played Fallon. Who took over from her?

14. Which three women monopolized the Snug of the Rover's Return in the early days of *Coronation Street*?

15. In *Home and Away*, how did Bobby receive her fatal injury?

16. *Falcon Crest* is set in which valley?

17. Who set fire to Frank's car lot in *Eastenders*?

18. Which member of the Ewing clan had heart surgery in *Dallas*?

19. In what street do the characters from *Neighbours* live?

20. Who shot Blake Carrington in the last episode of *Dynasty*?

21. In *Coronation Street*, which two friends run the cafe?

22. Who plays Greg Sumner in *Knots Landing*?

23. Who temporarily replaced Barbara Bel Geddes as Miss Ellie?

24. How did 'Dirty Den' die in *Eastenders*?

25. The spoof series *Soap* featured a butler who had his own spin-off series. What was his name?

1. What does the pH scale measure?

2. When growing seedlings, what is a cold frame used for?

3. What name is given to an insecticide which is absorbed into the plant sap stream from an application to the soil?

4. If a plant is described as 'suspensa', what does it mean?

5. What useful piece of gardening equipment did Edwin Beard Budding invent in 1830?

6. Fertilizers contain N P & K in various proportions. What do the initials stand for?

7. Which type of vegetable crop is most susceptible to damage from pests?

8. At what time of year would you divide chrysanthemums and michaelmas daisies?

9. Which of the following are grown from corms: hyacinth, gladiolus, daffodil, tulip, crocus?

10. In what part of the world have most successful seaside shrubs evolved?

11. What would you use secateurs for?

12. When a mulch is applied to the surface of the soil, what does it do?

13. What does it mean when a plant is named *exotica*?

14. What can be tent, barn or T-shaped?

15. Who sailed with Captain Cook to Australia and was responsible for bringing thousands of plants back to England, where he founded Kew Gardens?

16. Calcareous soils are rich in what?

17. Which crops can be sown earlier in open ground: onions or cauliflowers?

18. What name is given to a cross between botanically distinct species?

19. Blackberry bushes need lime-free soil. True or false?

20. When mowing a lawn, you might use a cylinder or a rotary mower. Which would you use if you wanted a striped effect?

21. Layering is a way of propagating plants. What does it mean?

22. What name is given to the type of weedkiller that does not kill established weeds but helps to prevent germination for up to three months?

23. Spinach will deteriorate if it is allowed to grow long enough to 'bolt'. What does that mean?

24. What does it mean if a plant is described as *prostratus*?

25. Among the most serious diseases that attack roses are black spot and rust. What type of diseases are these?

Q 1

1. Name the company headed by Richard Branson.

2. In which country is the town of Grozny, besieged by the Russians in 1994?

3. Who resigned as director of the CIA at the end of 1994?

4. In which country is the Zapatista guerilla movement active?

5. Who is Jean Luc Dehaene?

6. How did Dehaene hit the headlines in mid-1994?

7. Tony Blair is Leader of the Labour Party in Britain. What is his wife's name?

8. Who was returned to power in Haiti with American help?

9. Who became the Speaker of the House in America in 1995?

10. In 1997 the countries of the world begin work on a major space project to be completed in 2002. What is it?

11. Alija Izetbegovic is President of which country?

12. Eurotunnel has suffered a number of teething troubles, including too few passengers on the high-speed London-Paris and London-Brussels train service. What is this service called?

13. When did the IRA announce a complete cessation of military operations?

14. Which British bank crashed as a result of unwise derivatives trading?

15. Name the Formula One driver who agreed terms with McLaren and signed to partner Mika Hakkinen at the age of 42.

16. In Australia the OSW, created by the Whitlam government in 1974, was recently in the news. What do the initials stand for?

17. 2500 UN peacekeeping troops pulled out of which country in February 1995?

18. How many members did the European Union have in December 1994?

19. Which countries joined the European Union in January 1995?

20. Who was the first woman to head MI5?

21. Algeria has endured several years of conflict between the government and which extremist group?

22. Bill Gates has been called the richest man in America. How does he make his money?

23. Which country suffered a devastating earthquake in 1995?

24. In Britain, the ordination of women priests was adamantly opposed until recently. In which decade were women priests first allowed in New Zealand?

25. What is Bill Clinton's 'three strikes' policy?

1. In windsurfing, what is the uphaul?

2. How do wetsuits keep the wearer warm in water?

3. How many pieces are used in backgammon?

4. What name is given to computer games in which characters move from one level to another collecting objects to score points?

5. In what game do players 'peg out'?

6. How many dragon colours are there in mah jong?

7. When playing darts, the darts are thrown from behind a line. What is the line called?

8. What name is given to a kind of underwater hockey played between teams?

9. How many players take part in a game of Solo?

10. What are the crouch roll, pike fall and springheader?

11. What name is given to the horizontal lines of squares on a chessboard?

12. If you were rolling dice chanting 'baby needs new shoes' what would you be playing?

13. What does 'judo' mean?

14. What name is given to the flat surface of a skateboard?

15. How many skittles are used in table skittles?

16. 'Dungeons and Dragons' is one of the best known of the original computer games. What type of game is it?

17. In stud poker, how many cards are dealt before the betting starts?

18. How many pieces are there in a Rubik's cube?

19. What is BMX short for?

20. What is buddy diving?

21. In Scrabble, what bonus is gained if a player puts down all seven tiles in one turn?

22. What are PBM games?

23. In wild card poker, what is a wild card?

24. In the original Space Invaders, which is worth more points, a flying saucer or a column of space invaders?

25. What name is given to the gear system of racing and mountain bikes, whereby the chain is thrown from one sprocket onto the next?

1. What is Linford Christie's native country?

2. By what name is Edson Aro Arantes do Nascimento better known?

3. Racing driver Jochen Rindt suffered a fatal crash in practice for which event in 1970?

4. Who is regarded as the first boxing champion?

5. Why was Muhammad Ali stripped of his heavyweight title in 1967?

6. What ended the playing career of tennis star Arthur Ashe in 1979?

7. Who was the first man to sail non-stop round the world?

8. In which sport is Adrian Moorhouse well known?

9. Which US baseball player was once married to Marilyn Monroe?

10. Name the Canadian hockey player, probably the best in the history of the National Hockey League, who plays with the Edmonton Oilers and the Los Angeles Kings.

11. Josiah Shackford made the earliest known single-handed Atlantic crossing in 1786. Which country did he start from?

12. In which year did Daley Thompson first win the Olympic Decathlon?

13. In 1985, which 17-year-old was the youngest winner of the Wimbledon men's singles title?

14. Who has acted as captain most often in Test Matches?

15. Which British footballer was transferred to the Italian club Lazio in 1992 for £5.5 million?

16. The South African runner Zola Budd was given British citizenship to enable her to compete in the Olympic Games in which year?

17. Why is the New York Yankee stadium called 'the house that Ruth built'?

18. Who was the first French World Drivers Champion?

19. In which sport is Peter Oosterhuis well known?

20. Which heavyweight boxer was nicknamed the 'Manassa Mauler'?

21. Canadian sprinter Ben Johnson was disqualified from his winning event in 1983 for his use of steroids. In which event had he previously set a record?

22. Who was known as 'the Kaiser'?

23. Name the yachtsman who circumnavigated the world solo in 1970–71 and had previously rowed across the North Atlantic with a companion.

24. Graham Hick was his country's youngest professional cricketer at the age of 17. Which country was it?

25. Which woman was the outstanding athlete of the 1988 Olympics, winning three golds and a silver in sprints and relays?

1. Which country pioneered orienteering ?

2. What would you do with a cagoule?

3. Who led the team of mountaineers who first succeeded in climbing Everest?

4. What is a terminal moraine?

5. How long is a marathon?

6. When did the 'Golden Age of Mountaineering' – the 11 years in which 180 great peaks were climbed for the first time – begin?

7. In rock climbing, what does rappel mean?

8. What is the science of map-making called?

9. Which is the world's oldest annual race, which first took place in 1897?

10. Name the Alaskan mountain climbed for the first time in 1913.

11. Which athlete set a 100 metres record in Japan in 1991?

12. Which American broke that 1991 record in 1994?

13. In mountaineering, what is a cornice?

14. What would you do with dubbin?

15. On a snowy mountain, what is glissading?

16. Magnetic north is the north to which the compass needle always points. What is grid north?

17. When climbing, what would you be doing if you were traversing?

18. What name is given to metal spikes hammered into rock as anchors?

19. What is a couloir?

20. The first ascent of K2 was in 1954. What nationality was the team?

21. The Boston Marathon, run on or around April 19 every year, commemorates what event?

22. In mountaineering, what are the 'voies normales'?

23. Which is older, the London or the New York marathon?

24. In which year was the London Marathon first held?

25. In 1985 an American millionaire became, at 55, the oldest man to scale Everest and the first to climb to the highest points of all the continents. Name him.

Q ①

1. Which group's first album is *Piper at the Gate of Dawn*?

2. In which sport did Richard Meade become famous?

3. Who was the husband of Messalina?

4. Americans call it a bill. What is it called in Britain?

5. George IV tried to have his marriage to Caroline of Brunswick dissolved in 1820. On what grounds?

6. Which film featured the song 'Bright Eyes'?

7. Who painted the *Blue Boy*?

8. What is the name given to an area of low atmospheric pressure along the equator, and sometimes used for a person who is feeling depressed?

9. In which film did Marilyn Monroe sing 'That Old Black Magic'?

10. Mel Brooks is married to which actress?

11. What type of acid is normally used in car batteries?

12. What year links an overture by Tchaikovsky and Napoleon's retreat from Moscow?

13. What are the major suits in bridge?

14. Trevor Huddleston, a priest who later became an archbishop, wrote a book called *Naught for your Comfort*. What was it about?

15. What do superstitious actors call Shakespeare's *Macbeth*?

16. Who wrote about a traffic warden called Rita?

17. What, according to the saying, can you never make out of a sow's ear?

18. The Pole Star, the brightest star in the constellation of Ursa Minor, is known by what other name?

19. Who had a hit with 'The Ballad of Bonnie and Clyde'?

20. Cocker, clumber and springer are types of which breed of dog?

21. Bruce Willis, Sylvester Stallone and Arnold Schwarzenegger are the owners of which London restaurant?

22. What animal is a mandrill?

23. Name the Russian born novelist, a naturalized American, who wrote *The Fountainhead* and *Atlas Shrugged*.

24. In which sport might the participants have to battle through a tie-break?

25. What drink was often called 'old Tom'?

Answers to Quiz 13

Geography and Travel • European Tour

1. Marseilles
2. Dodona
3. Works of art collected mainly by Spanish royalty
4. Balmoral
5. Scenes from the 1066 Norman invasion of England
6. Geneva
7. The Vatican
8. Venice
9. Oberammergau
10. The free-standing campanile (bell-tower) of the cathedral
11. Île de la Cité
12. Dolomites
13. Spain
14. Mountains of Mourne
15. France
16. The Alps
17. The Creation
18. Siena
19. The White Tower
20. The Camargue
21. Avignon
22. Copenhagen
23. Spain
24. Mont Blanc
25. Hadrian's Wall

Popular Culture • Soaps: Then and Now

1. Stephanie Beacham
2. Jason Donovan
3. Zoe Tate and Beth Jordache
4. Pat Butcher
5. Summer Bay
6. Jock and Jason Ewing and Digger Barnes
7. Gioberti
8. Newton and Ridley
9. Bianca Jagger
10. Julie Martin
11. Grants
12. Lucy Ewing
13. Emma Samms
14. Ena Sharples, Martha Longhurst and Minnie Caldwell
15. In a speedboat incident
16. Tuscany valley
17. Phil Mitchell
18. Jock
19. Ramsay Street
20. Captain Handler
21. Gail Tilsley and Alma Barlow
22. William Devane
23. Donna Reed
24. He was shot
25. Benson

Indoors and Out • Gardening Know-how

1. Acidity and alkalinity of the soil
2. Hardening off the seedlings, so that they get used to outdoor conditions
3. Systemic
4. Hanging down or weeping
5. Lawnmower
6. Nitrogen, phosphorus, potassium
7. Members of the cabbage family
8. Spring
9. Gladiolus and crocus
10. Australia and New Zealand
11. Pruning
12. It prevents the growth of weeds and helps retain moisture
13. It is of foreign origin
14. Cloches
15. Joseph Banks
16. Chalk
17. Onions
18. Hybrid
19. True
20. Cylinder
21. Inducing a stem or shoot to grow roots while still attached to the parent plant
22. Residual weedkiller
23. Develop flowering shoots
24. It is ground-hugging
25. Fungal

Past and Present • In the News

1. Virgin
2. Chechnya
3. James Woolsey
4. Mexico
5. Prime Minister of Belgium
6. John Major vetoed him as European Union successor to Jacques Delors
7. Cherie
8. Jean-Bertrand Aristide
9. Newt Gingrich
10. The construction of Space Station Alpha
11. Bosnia
12. Eurostar
13. August 1994
14. Barings
15. Nigel Mansell
16. Office of Status of Women
17. Somalia
18. 12
19. Austria, Finland and Sweden
20. Stella Rimington
21. Islamic Salvation Front
22. In computer software
23. Japan
24. 1960s
25. The life sentence given to criminals found guilty three times of certain federal offences

Youth World • Fun and Games

1. The rope used to pull the sail out of the water
2. By trapping water between the body and the suit
3. 30
4. Platform
5. Cribbage
6. Three
7. The hockey
8. Octopush
9. Four
10. Dives
11. Ranks
12. Craps
13. The gentle way
14. Deck
15. Nine
16. A role-playing fantasy game
17. Two: one face up, one face down
18. 26
19. Bicycle Motocross
20. Diving with companions
21. 50 points
22. Play by mail games
23. It represents any card the player decides on
24. Flying saucer
25. Derailleur gear system

Famous Folk • Sporting Personalities

1. Jamaica
2. Pelé
3. Italian Grand Prix
4. James Figg
5. He refused to be drafted into the army
6. Heart trouble
7. Robin Knox-Johnston
8. Swimming
9. Joe Di Maggio
10. Wayne Gretzky
11. France
12. 1980
13. Boris Becker
14. Clive Lloyd
15. Paul Gascoigne
16. 1984
17. Baseball player Babe Ruth brought so much money to the club
18. Alain Prost
19. Golf
20. Jack Dempsey
21. 100 metres
22. Franz Beckenbauer
23. Chay Blyth
24. Zimbabwe
25. Florence Griffith-Joyner

Sport and Leisure • Walking, Running, Climbing

1. Sweden
2. Wear it
3. John Hunt
4. An accumulation of stones and debris left across a valley by a glacier which has since retreated
5. 42.195 km (26 miles 385 yards)
6. 1854
7. Descending by rope by means of mechanical brake devices
8. Cartography
9. Boston Marathon
10. Mount McKinley
11. Carl Lewis
12. Leroy Burrell
13. An overhanging mass of snow formed by the wind along the edge of a ridge
14. Put it on boots to keep them supple
15. A way of descending a snow slope by sliding
16. The north indicated by the grid on maps
17. Moving sideways without gaining altitude
18. Pitons (pins and pegs)
19. A gully or small open valley
20. Italian
21. Paul Revere's ride through Boston
22. The most regularly climbed routes
23. New York
24. 1981
25. Dick Bass

Pot Luck

1. Pink Floyd
2. Three-day eventing
3. Emperor Claudius
4. A banknote
5. Caroline's adultery
6. *Watership Down*
7. Thomas Gainsborough
8. Doldrums
9. *Bus Stop*
10. Anne Bancroft
11. Sulphuric acid
12. 1812
13. Spades and hearts
14. His experiences in South Africa
15. 'The Scottish Play'
16. Lennon and McCartney
17. A silk purse
18. North Star
19. Georgie Fame
20. Spaniel
21. Planet Hollywood
22. Baboon
23. Ayn Rand
24. Tennis
25. Gin

WHERE IN THE WORLD?

1. In which capital city would you travel on klongs and visit wats?

2. Which country produces most of the world's dates?

3. In which European mountain range is Andorra?

4. What country was once called Bechuanaland?

5. Where was Graham Greene's novel *The Comedians* set?

6. On which Hawaiian island is Waikiki beach?

7. In which country would you be if you lived in a houseboat on Dal Lake?

8. In which country does the heroine of *Shirley Valentine* take her life-changing holiday?

9. Which country has the oldest flag in the world?

10. In which city would you find the Spanish riding school with its famous Lippizaner horses?

11. 600 statues stand on Easter Island. In which ocean does this island lie?

12. Namè the country once known as Hibernia.

13. In which Australian territory is Ayers Rock?

14. Which countries are linked by the Khyber Pass?

15. Where would you find the ports of Limassol, Larnaca and Kyrenia?

16. Which is the only walled city in North America to be declared a World Heritage Treasure by UNESCO?

17. In which country would you find Cossack dancing?

18. Where would you travel on vaporetti instead of buses?

19. Which country has most borders with other countries?

20. Where would you find the geysers and hot springs of the Rotorua district?

21. If you were travelling through the Cascade Mountains, where would you be?

22. Which country has the red maple leaf on its flag?

23. Unique animal and bird species including platypus, wombat and kookaburra are found in which country?

24. Name the most prolific film-producing country in the world.

Q 8

25. Which island situated off the tip of the Sorrento peninsula in Italy has the Grotta Azura as one of its main tourist attractions?

5. Which story was filmed in 1925, 1943 and 1962 and was made into a musical by Andrew Lloyd Webber?

6. What power does the title character in *Carrie* possess?

7. Who is the father of *Rosemary's Baby*?

8. Which motel does Anthony Perkins run in *Psycho*?

9. Which actor became the archetypal monster with his starring role in Frankenstein in 1931?

10. Which character appears most often in horror films?

11. What is the name of the ghostly, scarred killer of *Nightmare on Elm Street* and several sequels?

12. Heather Langenkamp, who starred in *Nightmare on Elm Street*, played herself a decade later in another 'Nightmare' film. What was its title?

13. What is the name of the psychopathic killer played by Anthony Hopkins in *The Silence of the Lamb*s?

14. In which film does Vincent's Chucky doll come to life as a demonic killer?

15. Who plays the devil incarnate to three sex-starved witches in *The Witches of Eastwick*?

16. How old is the vampire telling his story to a journalist in *Interview with the Vampire*?

1. *The Fly*, a 1986 remake of the 1958 film, tells the story of a scientist who makes a mistake in an experiment and metamorphoses into a human fly. Who plays the scientist in the more recent film?

2. *The Innocents*, starring Deborah Kerr, was based on the novel *The Turn of the Screw*. Who wrote the novel?

3. Which film concerns a man-eating shark lurking off the beaches of a fictional resort called Amity?

4. Who directed *The Birds*?

17. Which 13-year-old actress is *The Little Girl Who Lives Down the Lane* in the 1977 Canadian film?

18. In *Cape Fear* Robert de Niro plays ex-convict Max Cady, who terrorizes a lawyer's family. Who plays the role in the previous version in 1962?

19. What is the link between Harvey Stephens, Jonathan Scott-Taylor and Sam Neill, stars of a trio of horror films?

20. In the 1958 Hammer film *Dracula* (in the US *The Horror of Dracula*) Peter Cushing plays Van Helsing. Who plays Dracula?

21. Which spoof horror film, which has become a cult movie, includes the songs 'Dammit Janet', 'The Time Warp' and 'Touch Me'?

22. Who directed the 1994 film *Mary Shelley's Frankenstein*?

23. In *The Shining*, based on Stephen King's novel, what is 'shining'?

24. Some critics compare *Halloween* to *Psycho*, which stars Janet Leigh. Name her daughter, who stars in *Halloween*.

25. Heather O'Rouke plays a child stalked by evil spirits in *Poltergeist* and its two sequels. What is the child's name?

1. What are sometimes known as cake urchins or sea biscuits?

2. How does a cuttlefish catch its prey?

3. What type of creature is a mudskipper?

4. Which group of creatures includes slugs, snails, octopuses and chitons?

5. What are the two basic types of barnacle?

6. How did the lantern fish get its name?

7. What can be cut-throat, moray or culper?

8. What is the study of shells called?

9. Why is a pilot fish so called?

10. How does a mussel feed?

11. Horns made from shells have been used by many civilizations. Which shells are usually used?

12. Lobsters are red when cooked. What colour are they when alive?

13. Dolphins live together in groups. What are these groups called?

14. How can dolphins be distinguished from porpoises?

15. What is a young pilchard called?

16. Why is the basking shark harmless?

17. How do hermit crabs differ from other crabs?

18. Lampreys are jawless fish. How do they feed?

19. What are oarweed, furbelows and dabberlocks?

20. Why do divers often fear barracudas more than sharks?

21. Abalones are sea snails. What is the abalone or ear shell best known for?

22. How does the scorpion fish get its name?

23. Helmet shells take their name from their resemblance to the helmets of Roman gladiators. What item of jewellery is traditionally carved from bullmouth helmet shells?

24. Which fish uses a 'rod and line' to catch other fish, using a long fin growing from its forehead, with a lure-like a bait on the end of it?

25. Which are the largest whales?

Q 23

1. The world's most powerful warship to date was launched in 1907. What was it called?

2. The final section of the longest continuous stretch of railway in the world was completed in 1917. Name the railway.

3. Emily Davison threw herself in front of the King's horse at the Derby in 1913. What cause was she trying to promote?

4. Who were the original allies of the British Empire in World War I?

5. One of the factors that brought the United States into the First World War was the sinking of a British liner which was carrying Americans. Name the liner.

6. Britain's War Minister appeared on the famous World War I recruiting poster. Who was he?

7. The League of Nations was formed in 1919. What did it become in 1945?

8. Where was Hitler when he wrote *Mein Kampf*?

9. Which English-speaking country gave women the vote in 1901?

10. Which country built the series of fortifications called the Siegfried Line?

11. Which British prime minister announced in 1937 that the result of a European conference would guarantee 'peace in our time'?

12. In 1940 a fleet of small ships evacuated British and French troops from which port?

13. About what battle did Churchill say 'Never in the field of human conflict was so much owed by so many to so few'?

14. Which Russian city was cut off by the Germans for nearly 18 months in the early 1940s?

15. What name was given to the atomic bomb that devastated Nagasaki in 1945?

16. Which European city was blockaded by the Russians after World War II and was saved by a massive airlift of supplies?

17. What popular name was given to the European Recovery Programme which provided aid for rebuilding after World War II?

18. What was tested on Bikini Atoll in the Pacific in 1954?

19. Name the first space traveller in Sputnik II.

20. Which President brought American troops out of Vietnam?

21. When the Viet Cong took over Saigon, what did they name it?

22. The eastern region of Nigeria declared independence in 1968, but the country was united again in 1970. What was the independent republic called?

23. Ian Smith was premier of which country?

24. Under what name do we know Vladimir Ilyich Ulyanov?

25. The Berlin Wall was breached in 1989. For how long had the border been closed?

1. Who plays the robot gunfighter in *Westworld*?

2. Name the director of *Close Encounters of the Third Kind*.

3. What is a cyborg?

4. Ian Holm plays Ash in *Alien*. What is odd about Ash?

5. Who wrote the first major novel about a war with alien invaders?

6. In the *Six Million Dollar Man* who was the actress who played the Bionic Man's wife?

7. Who was the actress who played the female equivalent of the Bionic Man?

8. In the classic film *The Invasion of the Body Snatchers*, where do the duplicate bodies grow, in preparation for their takeover?

9. Who plays *The Prisoner*?

10. *Cocoon* tells the story of the members of a retirement community who are rejuvenated when a group of aliens take up residence nearby. Where is the action set?

11. What is cryogenics?

12. In what car does Michael J. Fox go to the future?

13. William Shatner as James Kirk is the first captain of the starship Enterprise. Who is the second?

14. In which *Star Trek* film does the crew go back to 20th-century Earth to collect whales?

Q13

17. Which pop star plays an alien in *The Man Who Fell to Earth*?

18. In which TV series is Dr David Banner strangely transformed when he becomes angry?

19. *Star Wars* is the first film of a trilogy. Name the other two films.

20. In which novel and film do mobile giant plants attack humans?

21. Which character makes a series of quantum leaps?

22. In *Planet of the Apes*, what proves to the hero that the world he knows has been blown up?

23. Who stars in the title role of *The New Adventures of Superman*?

24. In *Total Recall* Schwarzenegger stars as a construction worker who comes to believe that he is a secret agent. Which planet does he travel to in order to discover the truth?

15. In what year is the TV series *Babylon 5* set?

16. The TV series *Battlestar Galactica* was the subject of lawsuits from 20th-Century Fox because they alleged it was a 'steal' from which film?

25. Which author wrote the famous *Foundation* saga that won the Hugo Award for Best All-Time Novel Series?

Q19

1. What was distinctive about the appearance of Israeli commander General Moshe Dayan?

2. General Eisenhower commanded US forces in Europe in World War ll and later became the US President. Which party did he represent?

3. Which Carthaginian general took elephants and troops over the Alps?

4. What date was predicted as the date of Julius Caesar's death?

5. Which American general led the Confederate armies in their only run of successes in the Civil War?

6. What relation was Earl Mountbatten of Burma to Queen Victoria?

7. Which Chinese general set up the right-wing government in Taiwan in 1949 when he was expelled from the mainland by Communist forces?

8. Which German field marshall was played by James Mason in the 1951 film?

9. Who led the Boer army against the British and became Prime Minister of South Africa in 1910?

10. Which English soldier and statesman created the New Model Army?

11. Under what name do we know Francisco Paulino Hermengildo Teodulo Franco y Bahamonde?

12. In 1429 Joan of Arc led the French army to victory over the English. Which city were they besieging?

13. General de Gaulle was a gallant soldier and President of France from 1956 to 1969. What is the appropriate meaning of the name 'de Gaulle'?

14. Which 19th-century South American leader was known as the Liberator?

15. Where was Napoleon exiled in 1813?

16. After his final defeat at Waterloo in 1815, where was Napoleon exiled?

17. Name the general who commanded the US forces in the Far East in World War II and in the Korean War.

18. Which Roman statesman and general married Caesar's only daughter Julia, though he later led forces against Caesar in the civil war?

19. Give the first names of Viscount Montgomery of Alamein.

20. Which British general was besieged at Khartoum in 1885?

21. Who played the title role in the 1970 film *Patton: Lust for Glory*?

22. Which Marshal of France was appointed Commander-in-Chief of the Allied armies in 1918?

23. Claus von Stauffenberg, the World War II German general, is best remembered for what?

24. For what brutal action of the American Civil War is General Sherman best remembered?

25. Which revolutionary leader, whose first name was Ernesto, adopted the name Che?

Q 4

Q 25

4. Which team won a record fifth Super Bowl title in American football in January 1995?

5. How many forwards are there on each side in hockey?

6. How does the size of teams differ in Rugby League and Rugby Union?

7. A record transfer fee was paid by Juventus to Bari for which Association Football player?

8. The first women's soccer World Cup was held in China in 1991. Who won?

9. In Rugby, where does the ball go when it goes into touch?

10. Australian Rules Football is unique to Australia. How many team-members are playing at any one time?

11. What, in American football, is spearing?

12. American footballer George Blanda holds the record for the number of games played in the NFL. How many seasons did he play?

13. Which country won the World Cup for the fourth time in 1994?

14. Women's lacrosse has 12 team-members playing at any one time. How many does men's lacrosse have?

1. Which Brazilian World Cup star was known as 'the little bird'?

2. In the World Cup, which was the first country to win the Jules Rimet trophy twice?

3. In American football, how many points are awarded for a field goal?

Q 7

15. American football is a fast-growing sport in Europe. When was the European Football League formed?

16. In American football, what is a pass that travels either behind or along the line of the scrimmage called?

17. Name the nations that take part in the Five Nations Rugby Championships.

18. How many times has Switzerland, home of FIFA, staged the World Cup?

19. Where was the rugby World Cup played in May and June 1995?

20. The first Olympic hockey game was played in 1908. Who won?

21. In which country was the hockey World Cup first played on an artificial surface?

22. The Big Four Bowl games in American football include the Rose Bowl and Cotton Bowl. Name the other two.

23. Which English footballer was known as 'the wizard of the dribble'?

24. In soccer, what is an indirect free kick?

25. Which French Rugby Union player gained his hundredth cap in 1994?

Q 9

1. Where would you visit the Great Slave Lake?

2. In Cecil B. De Mille's name, what does the initial B stand for?

3. Which East German ice skater was 1984 Olympic champion and by 1990 had won four world titles?

4. The TV series *Inspector Morse* is set in which English town?

5. In the Bible, who wore a coat of many colours?

6. Sodium hydroxide is commonly known by what name?

7. What is the general term used to describe the islands of the central and south Pacific, including Australia and New Zealand?

8. At which festival is the Golden Rose award given?

9. In the 1958 film *Summer Holiday*, where was Cliff Richard's double-decker bus heading?

10. What branch of science deals with heat and energy?

11. In Roman times, by what name was Istanbul known?

12. Where would you find a crevasse?

13. What is the popular name for timpani?

14. In which country would you find the Sutherland Waterfall?

15. Who, in the nursery rhyme, had 10,000 men?

16. In the Bible, which is the shortest of the four Gospels?

17. Which film did the Beatles make for television?

18. What colour sari would a Hindu bride wear?

19. In the TV series *Happy Days*, what was Fonz's first name?

20. How many parts of speech are there?

21. What type of food is Dunlop?

22. The Nazis invaded which part of Britain in 1940?

23. Complete this quotation from Shaw's *Man and Superman*: 'It is a woman's business to get married as soon as possible and a man's . . .'

24. In computer language, what name is given to the part of the memory which holds data while it is waiting to be used?

25. What do D. H. Lawrence's initials stand for?

Geography and Travel • Where in the World?

1. Bangkok
2. Iraq
3. Pyrenees
4. Botswana
5. Haiti
6. Oahu
7. Kashmir
8. Greece
9. Denmark
10. Vienna
11. Pacific
12. Ireland
13. Northern Territory
14. Pakistan and
 Afghanistan
15. Cyprus
16. Quebec
17. Russia
18. Venice
19. China
20. North Island of New Zealand
21. Washington State, USA
22. Canada
23. Australia
24. India
25. Capri

Popular Culture • Horror Movies

1. Jeff Goldblum
2. Henry James
3. *Jaws*
4. Alfred Hitchcock
5. *Phantom of the Opera*
6. Telekinesis
7. Satan
8. Bates Motel
9. Boris Karloff
10. Dracula
11. Freddy Krueger
12. *Wes Craven's New Nightmare*
13. Hannibal Lector
14. *Child's Play*
15. Jack Nicholson
16. 200 years
17. Jodie Foster
18. Robert Mitchum
19. They all play Damien, the anti-Christ, in *The Omen* and its sequels
20. Christopher Lee
21. *The Rocky Horror Picture Show*
22. Kenneth Branagh
23. Psychic ability
24. Jamie Lee Curtis
25. Carol Anne

Indoors and Out • Sea and Shore

1. Sand dollars
2. It shoots out long tentacles at speed
3. Fish
4. Molluscs
5. Acorn and goose
6. It has a row of light-producing organs down each side of its body
7. Eels
8. Conchology
9. It swims close to larger fishes as though guiding them
10. By filtering small particles from water
11. Conch and triton
12. Blue
13. Schools
14. By their beaked snouts
15. Sardine
16. It feeds on plankton only
17. Their rear part is not covered by shell
18. They are parasites, preying on other fish by sucking their blood
19. Seaweeds
20. They hunt by sight and will attack any flashing metal object
21. The rainbow mother-of-pearl sheen on the inside of the shell
22. From its many sharp spines, which can be poisonous
23. Cameo brooches
24. Angler fish
25. Blue whales

Past and Present • Making of the Modern World

1. *HMS Dreadnought*
2. Trans-Siberian Railway
3. Women's suffrage
4. France and Russia
5. *Lusitania*
6. Lord Kitchener
7. United Nations
8. In jail
9. Australia
10. Germany
11. Neville Chamberlain
12. Dunkirk
13. Battle of Britain
14. Leningrad
15. Fat boy
16. Berlin
17. The Marshall Plan
18. The hydrogen bomb
19. Laika, a dog
20. Nixon
21. Ho Chi Minh City
22. Biafra
23. Rhodesia
24. Lenin
25. 28 years

Youth World • Science Fiction

1. Yul Brynner
2. Steven Spielberg
3. Part man, part machine
4. He is a malfunctioning android
5. H.G. Wells
6. Farrah Fawcett-Major
7. Lindsay Wagner
8. In pods
9. Patrick McGoohan
10. Florida
11. The science of freezing living creatures and bringing them back to
 life again
12. DeLorean
13. Captain Picard, played by Patrick Stewart
14. *Star Trek IV. The Voyage Home*
15. 2259
16. *Star Wars*
17. David Bowie
18. *The Incredible Hulk*
19. *The Empire Strikes Back* and *Return of the Jedi*
20. *The Day of the Triffids*
21. Dr Sam Beckett
22. The remains of the Statue of Liberty
23. Dean Cain
24. Mars
25. Isaac Asimov

Famous Folk • Military Leaders

1. He wore a black eye-patch
2. Republican
3. Hannibal
4. The Ides of March (15 March)
5. Stonewall Jackson
6. Great-grandson
7. Chiang Kai-Shek
8. Rommel
9. Louis Botha
10. Oliver Cromwell
11. General Franco
12. Orléans
13. 'Of France'
14. Simón Bolívar
15. Elba
16. St Helena
17. General Douglas MacArthur
18. Pompey
19. Bernard Law
20. General Gordon
21. George C. Scott
22. Foch
23. The conspiracy to assassinate Hitler
24. The destructive march
 through Georgia and burning of Atlanta
25. Che Guevara

Sport and Leisure • On the Field

1. Garrincha
2. Italy
3. Three
4. San Francisco 49ers
5. Five
6. Rugby League has 13 players a side, Rugby Union has 15
7. David Platt
8. USA
9. Out of play over the sidelines
10. 18
11. Diving head-first at an
 opposing player
12. 26
13. Brazil
14. 10 in each team
15. 1985
16. A lateral
17. England, Ireland, Scotland, Wales and France
18. Once
19. South Africa
20. Scotland
21. Canada
22. Super Bowl and Orange
 Bowl
23. Stanley Matthews
24. A kick from which a goal cannot be scored until the ball has been touched by another player
25. Philippe Sella

Pot Luck

1. Canada
2. Blount
3. Katarina Witt
4. Oxford
5. Joseph
6. Caustic soda
7. Oceania
8. Montreux
9. Athens
10. Thermodynamics
11. Byzantium
12. In a glacier
13. Kettledrums
14. New Zealand
15. The grand old Duke of York
16. Mark
17. *Magical Mystery Tour*
18. Red
19. Arthur
20. Eight
21. Cheese
22. Channel Islands
23. 'To keep unmarried for as long as he can'
24. Buffer
25. David Herbert

INDEX

Picture Acknowledgements:

(Abbreviations Key: T = Top, B = Below)

Barnaby's Picture Library: 10, 15, 16, 23, 24 (Gerald Cubitt), 28 T, 36, 37, 39, 43 (B. Gibbs), 46 (David W. Corson), 50, 51, 54 T, 58, 59, 69, 72, 73, 74, 79, 82, 87, 90, 95, 101, 104, 105, 107 (Lesley Howling), 121, 123, 124 (G. Clyde), 126, 127, 128, 132, 137 T, 141, 145, 154 (H. Kanus), 158, 159, 162, 163, 169, 172, 176, 177, 195, 203 (© Richard Gardner), 212, 216, 220 T, 222 (Andrew Besley), 244. **Popperfoto**: 11, 12, 13, 18, 21, 22, 28 B, 29, 34, 42, 48, 49, 53, 55, 56, 57, 64, 68, 71, 75, 77, 78, 83, 84 (Both), 85, 86, 88, 93, 100, 106, 108 TL, 110, 111, 112, 113, 118, 119 (© David Brown), 125, 129, 131, 136, 137 B, 139, 140, 142 (Greg Newton), 144, 154, 156, 157, 160, 161, 166, 167, 173, 178, 179, 182, 183, 185, 187 (Bob Thomas), 190, 191, 193, 196, 204, 208, 209, 214, 220 B, 221, 223, 229, 230, 232, 233 (© Hector Mata), 234, 235 (Bob Thomas), 238, 239, 240, 248, 251, 252, 253, 256, 257, 258 (Bob Thomas). **Hulton Deutsch Collection**: 14, 17, 20 (Both), 35, 38 (Both), 47, 52, 54 B, 60 B, 65, 70, 76, 89, 92, 94, 96, 97, 102, 108 B, 109, 130, 143, 146, 147, 150, 168 (Mckenzie), 174, 175, 184, 196, 198, 200, 201, 202, 205, 210, 215, 218, 219, 226, 227, 236, 237, 250, 254, 255, 259. **Kobal Collection**: 19, 25, 30, 31, 60 T, 91, 103, 114, 115, 120, 138, 151, 164, 165, 180, 181, 186, 192, 211, 217, 228, 241, 245, 246, 247. **Robert Harding Picture Library**: 40, 41, 231, 248. **Syndication International**: 61, 66, 67 (Both), 194 (Bernard Alfieri). **Bridgeman Art Library** 133, 148 (all), 149, 199. **Haldane Mason**: 32, 33, 122. **Frank Lane Photo Agency**: 213 (© Mark Newman)

Every effort has been made to trace the copyright holders and we apologise in advance for any unintentional omissions. We would be pleased to insert the appropriate acknowledgement in any subsequent edition of this publication.